Teacher Edition

Eureka Math®
Grade 6
Module 2

Special thanks go to the Gordon A. Cain Center and to the Department of Mathematics at Louisiana State University for their support in the development of *Eureka Math*.

For a free *Eureka Math* Teacher
Resource Pack, Parent Tip
Sheets, and more please visit
https://eurekamath.greatminds.org/teacher-resource-pack

Published by Great Minds.

Printed in the U.S.A.

This book may be purchased from the publisher at eureka-math.org

BAB 10 9 8 7 6 5 4 3 2

ISBN 978-1-63255-386-7

Eureka Math: A Story of Ratios® Contributors

Michael Allwood, Curriculum Writer
Tiah Alphonso, Program Manager—Curriculum Production
Catriona Anderson, Program Manager—Implementation Support
Beau Bailey, Curriculum Writer
Scott Baldridge, Lead Mathematician and Lead Curriculum Writer
Bonnie Bergstresser, Math Auditor
Gail Burrill, Curriculum Writer
Beth Chance, Statistician
Joanne Choi, Curriculum Writer
Jill Diniz, Program Director
Lori Fanning, Curriculum Writer
Ellen Fort, Math Auditor
Kathy Fritz, Curriculum Writer
Glenn Gebhard, Curriculum Writer
Krysta Gibbs, Curriculum Writer
Winnie Gilbert, Lead Writer / Editor, Grade 8
Pam Goodner, Math Auditor
Debby Grawn, Curriculum Writer
Bonnie Hart, Curriculum Writer
Stefanie Hassan, Lead Writer / Editor, Grade 8
Sherri Hernandez, Math Auditor
Bob Hollister, Math Auditor
Patrick Hopfensperger, Curriculum Writer
Sunil Koswatta, Mathematician, Grade 8
Brian Kotz, Curriculum Writer
Henry Kranendonk, Lead Writer / Editor, Statistics
Connie Laughlin, Math Auditor
Jennifer Loftin, Program Manager—Professional Development
Nell McAnelly, Project Director
Ben McCarty, Mathematician
Stacie McClintock, Document Production Manager
Saki Milton, Curriculum Writer
Pia Mohsen, Curriculum Writer
Jerry Moreno, Statistician
Ann Netter, Lead Writer / Editor, Grades 6–7
Sarah Oyler, Document Coordinator
Roxy Peck, Statistician, Lead Writer / Editor, Statistics
Terrie Poehl, Math Auditor
Kristen Riedel, Math Audit Team Lead
Spencer Roby, Math Auditor
Kathleen Scholand, Math Auditor
Erika Silva, Lead Writer / Editor, Grade 6–7
Robyn Sorenson, Math Auditor
Hester Sutton, Advisor / Reviewer Grades 6–7
Shannon Vinson, Lead Writer / Editor, Statistics
Allison Witcraft, Math Auditor

Julie Wortmann, Lead Writer / Editor, Grade 7
David Wright, Mathematician, Lead Writer / Editor, Grades 6–7

Mathematics Curriculum

6 GRADE

Table of Contents[1]

Arithmetic Operations Including Division of Fractions

---

[1]Each lesson is ONE day, and ONE day is considered a 45-minute period.

Topics A through D (assessment 1 day, return 1 day, remediation or further applications 1 day)

EUREKA
MATH

Grade 6 • Module 2

Arithmetic Operations Including Division of Fractions

OVERVIEW

In Module 1, students used their existing understanding of multiplication and division as they began their study of ratios and rates. In Module 2, students complete their understanding of the four operations as they study division of whole numbers, division by a fraction, and operations on multi-digit decimals. This expanded understanding serves to complete their study of the four operations with positive rational numbers, thereby preparing students for understanding, locating, and ordering negative rational numbers (Module 3) and algebraic expressions (Module 4).

In Topic A, students extend their previous understanding of multiplication and division to divide fractions by fractions. They construct division stories and solve word problems involving division of fractions (**6.NS.A.1**). Through the context of word problems, students understand and use partitive division of fractions to determine how much is in each group. They explore real-life situations that require them to ask, "How much is one share?" and "What part of the unit is that share?" Students use measurement to determine quotients of fractions. They are presented conceptual problems where they determine that the quotient represents how many of the divisor is in the dividend. For example, students understand that $\frac{6 \text{ cm}}{2 \text{ cm}}$ derives a quotient of 3 because 2 divides into 6 three times. They apply this method to quotients of fractions, understanding $\frac{6}{7} \div \frac{2}{7} = \frac{6 \text{ sevenths}}{2 \text{ sevenths}} = 3$ because, again, 2 divides into 6 three times. Students look for and uncover patterns while modeling quotients of fractions to ultimately discover the relationship between multiplication and division. Using this relationship, students create equations and formulas to represent and solve problems. Later in the module, students learn the direct correlation of division of fractions to division of decimals along with the application of this concept.

Prior to division of decimals, students revisit all decimal operations in Topic B. Students have had extensive experience with decimal operations to the hundredths and thousandths (**5.NBT.B.7**), which prepares them to easily compute with more decimal places. Students begin by relating the first lesson in this topic to the last lesson in Topic A, which focused on mixed numbers. They find that sums and differences of large mixed numbers can sometimes be more efficiently determined by first converting the number to a decimal and then applying the standard algorithms (**6.NS.B.3**). They use estimation to justify their answers.

Within decimal multiplication, students begin to practice the distributive property. Students use arrays and partial products to understand and apply the distributive property as they solve multiplication problems involving decimals. By gaining fluency in the distributive property throughout this module and the next, students become proficient in applying the distributive property in Module 4 (**6.EE.A.3**). Estimation and place value enable students to determine the placement of the decimal point in products and recognize that the size of a product is relative to each factor. Students learn to use connections between fraction multiplication and decimal multiplication.

In Grades 4 and 5, students used concrete models, pictorial representations, and properties to divide whole numbers (**4.NBT.B.6, 5.NBT.B.6**). They became efficient in applying the standard algorithm for long division. Students broke dividends apart into like base ten units, applying the distributive property to find quotients place by place. In Topic C, students connect estimation to place value and determine that the standard algorithm is simply a tally system arranged in place value columns (**6.NS.B.2**). Students understand that when they "bring down" the next digit in the algorithm, they are essentially distributing, recording, and shifting to the next place value. They understand that the steps in the algorithm continually provide better approximations to the answer. Students further their understanding of division as they develop fluency in the use of the standard algorithm to divide multi-digit decimals (**6.NS.B.3**). They make connections to division of fractions and rely on mental math strategies to implement the division algorithm when finding the quotients of decimals.

In the final topic, students think logically about multiplicative arithmetic. In Topic D, students apply odd and even number properties and divisibility rules to find factors and multiples. They extend this application to consider common factors and multiples and find greatest common factors and least common multiples. Students explore and discover that Euclid's algorithm is a more efficient way to find the greatest common factor of larger numbers and see that Euclid's algorithm is based on long division.

The module comprises 19 lessons; six days are reserved for administering the Mid- and End-of-Module Assessments, returning the assessments, and remediating or providing further applications of the concepts. The Mid-Module Assessment follows Topic B. The End-of-Module Assessment follows Topic D.

Focus Standards

Apply and extend previous understandings of multiplication and division to divide fractions by fractions.

6.NS.A.1   Interpret and compute quotients of fractions, and solve word problems involving division of fractions by fractions, e.g., by using visual fraction models and equations to represent the problem. *For example, create a story context for* $(2/3) \div (3/4)$ *and use a visual fraction model to show the quotient; use the relationship between multiplication and division to explain that* $(2/3) \div (3/4) = 8/9$ *because* $3/4$ *of* $8/9$ *is* $2/3$. *(In general,* $(a/b) \div (c/d) = ad/bc$.) *How much chocolate will each person get if 3 people share* $1/2$ *lb of chocolate equally? How many* $3/4$-*cup servings are in* $2/3$ *of a cup of yogurt? How wide is a rectangular strip of land with length* $3/4$ *mi and area* $1/2$ *square mi?*

Compute fluently with multi-digit numbers and find common factors and multiples.

6.NS.B.2   Fluently divide multi-digit numbers using the standard algorithm.

6.NS.B.3   Fluently add, subtract, multiply, and divide multi-digit decimals using the standard algorithm for each operation.

Module 2:   Arithmetic Operations Including Division of Fractions

6.NS.B.4   Find the greatest common factor of two whole numbers less than or equal to 100 and the least common multiple of two whole numbers less than or equal to 12. Use the distributive property to express a sum of two whole numbers 1–100 with a common factor as a multiple of a sum of two whole numbers with no common factor. *For example, express* $36 + 8$ *as* $4(9 + 2)$.

Foundational Standards

Gain familiarity with factors and multiples.

4.OA.B.4   Find all factor pairs for a whole number in the range 1–100. Recognize that a whole number is a multiple of each of its factors. Determine whether a given whole number in the range 1–100 is a multiple of a given one-digit number. Determine whether a given whole number in the range 1–100 is prime or composite.

Understand the place value system.

5.NBT.A.2   Explain patterns in the number of zeros of the product when multiplying a number by powers of 10, and explain patterns in the placement of the decimal point when a decimal is multiplied or divided by a power of 10. Use whole-number exponents to denote powers of 10.

Perform operations with multi-digit whole numbers and with decimals to hundredths.

5.NBT.B.6   Find whole-number quotients of whole numbers with up to four-digit dividends and two-digit divisors, using strategies based on place value, the properties of operations, and/or the relationship between multiplication and division. Illustrate and explain the calculation by using equations, rectangular arrays, and/or area models.

5.NBT.B.7   Add, subtract, multiply, and divide decimals to hundredths, using concrete models or drawings and strategies based on place value, properties of operations, and/or the relationship between addition and subtraction; relate the strategy to a written method and explain the reasoning used.

Apply and extend previous understandings of multiplication and division to multiply and divide fractions.

5.NF.B.4   Apply and extend previous understandings of multiplication to multiply a fraction or whole number by a fraction.

a.   Interpret the product $(a/b) \times q$ as a parts of a partition of q into b equal parts; equivalently, as the result of a sequence of operations $a \times q \div b$. *For example, use a visual fraction model to show* $(2/3) \times 4 = 8/3$, *and create a story context for this equation. Do the same with* $(2/3) \times (4/5) = 8/15$. *(In general,* $(a/b) \times (c/d) = ac/bd$.)

Module 2:   Arithmetic Operations Including Division of Fractions   5

© 2015 Great Minds. eureka-math.org
G6-M2-TE-B2-1.3.1-01.2016

5.NF.B.7 Apply and extend previous understandings of division to divide unit fractions by whole numbers and whole numbers by fractions.[2]

a. Interpret division of a unit fraction by a non-zero whole number, and compute such quotients. *For example, create a story context for (1/3) ÷ 4, and use a visual fraction model to show the quotient. Use the relationship between multiplication and division to explain that (1/3) ÷ 4 = 1/12 because (1/12) × 4 = 1/3.*

b. Interpret division of a whole number by a unit fraction, and compute such quotients. *For example, create a story context for 4 ÷ (1/5), and use a visual fraction model to show the quotient. Use the relationship between multiplication and division to explain that 4 ÷ (1/5) = 20 because 20 × (1/5) = 4.*

Focus Standards for Mathematical Practice

MP.1 **Make sense of problems and persevere in solving them.** Students use concrete representations when understanding the meaning of division and apply it to the division of fractions. They ask themselves, "What is this problem asking me to find?" For instance, when determining the quotient of fractions, students ask themselves how many sets or groups of the divisor are in the dividend. That quantity is the quotient of the problem. They solve simpler problems to gain insight into the solution. They confirm, for example, that $10 \div 2$ can be found by determining how many groups of two are in ten. They apply that strategy to the division of fractions. Students may use pictorial representations such as area models, array models, number lines, and drawings to conceptualize and solve problems.

MP.2 **Reason abstractly and quantitatively.** Students make sense of quantities and their relationships in problems. They understand "how many" as it pertains to the divisor in a quotient of fractions problem. They understand and use connections between divisibility and the greatest common factor to apply the distributive property. Students consider units and labels for numbers in contextual problems and consistently refer to what the labels represent to make sense in the problem. Students rely on estimation and properties of operations to justify the reason for their answers when manipulating decimal numbers and their operations. Students reason abstractly when applying place value and fraction sense when determining the placement of a decimal point.

MP.6 **Attend to precision.** Students use precise language and place value when adding, subtracting, multiplying, and dividing by multi-digit decimal numbers. Students read decimal numbers using place value. For example, 326.31 is read as three hundred twenty-six and thirty-one hundredths. Students calculate sums, differences, products, and quotients of decimal numbers with a degree of precision appropriate to the problem context.

---

[2]Students who are able to multiply fractions in general can develop strategies to divide fractions in general by reasoning about the relationship between multiplication and division. But division of a fraction by a fraction is not a requirement in Grade 5.

MP.7   **Look for and make use of structure.** Students find patterns and connections when multiplying and dividing multi-digit decimals. For instance, they use place value to recognize that the quotient of $22.5 \div 0.15$ is the same as the quotient of $2250 \div 15$. In the example $36 + 48 = 12(3 + 4)$, students recognize that when expressing the sum of two whole numbers using the distributive property, the number 12 represents the greatest common factor of 36 and 48 and that 36 and 48 are both multiples of 12. When dividing fractions, students recognize and make use of a related multiplication problem or create a number line and use skip-counting to determine the number of times the divisor is added to obtain the dividend. Students use the familiar structure of long division to find the greatest common factor in another way, specifically the Euclidean algorithm.

MP.8   **Look for and express regularity in repeated reasoning.** Students determine reasonable answers to problems involving operations with decimals. Estimation skills and compatible numbers are used. For instance, when 24.385 is divided by 3.91, students determine that the answer is close to the quotient of $24 \div 4$, which equals 6. Students discover, relate, and apply strategies when problem solving, such as the use of the distributive property to solve a multiplication problem involving fractions and/or decimals (e.g., $350 \times 1.8 = 350(1 + 0.8) = 350 + 280 = 630$). When dividing fractions, students may use the following reasoning: Since $\frac{2}{7} + \frac{2}{7} + \frac{2}{7} = \frac{6}{7}$, then $\frac{6}{7} \div \frac{2}{7} = 3$, so I can solve fraction division problems by first getting common denominators and then solving the division problem created by the numerators. Students understand the long division algorithm and the continual breakdown of the dividend into different place value units. Further, students use those repeated calculations and reasoning to determine the greatest common factor of two numbers using the Euclidean algorithm.

Terminology

New or Recently Introduced Terms

- **Greatest Common Factor** (The *greatest common factor* of two whole numbers (not both zero) is the greatest whole number that is a factor of each number.

  For example, the GCF of 24 and 36 is 12 because when all of the whole number factors of 24 and 36 are listed, the largest factor they share is 12.)

- **Least Common Multiple** (The *least common multiple* of two whole numbers is the smallest whole number greater than zero that is a multiple of each number.

  For example, the LCM of 4 and 6 is 12 because when the multiples of 4 and 6 are listed, the smallest or first multiple they share is 12.)

- **Multiplicative Inverses** (A *multiplicative inverse of a number* is a number such that the product of both numbers is 1.

  For example, $\frac{3}{4}$ and $\frac{4}{3}$ are multiplicative inverses of one another because $\frac{3}{4} \times \frac{4}{3} = \frac{4}{3} \times \frac{3}{4} = 1$.

  Multiplicative inverses do not always have to be the reciprocal. For example, $\frac{1}{5}$ and $\frac{10}{2}$ both have a product of 1, which makes them multiplicative inverses of each other.)

Familiar Terms and Symbols[3]

- Algorithm
- Composite Number
- Distributive Property
- Dividend
- Divisor
- Estimate
- Factors
- Multiples
- Prime Number
- Reciprocal

Suggested Tools and Representations

- Counters
- Fraction Tiles (example shown to the right)
- Tape Diagrams
- Area Models (example shown below)

For example: $\frac{3}{4} \div \frac{1}{2}$

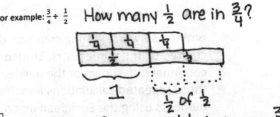

$\frac{2}{5} \div 5$

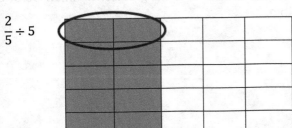

Assessment Summary

Assessment Type	Administered	Format	Standards Addressed
Mid-Module Assessment Task	After Topic B	Constructed response with rubric	6.NS.A.1, 6.NS.B.3
End-of-Module Assessment Task	After Topic D	Constructed response with rubric	6.NS.A.1, 6.NS.B.2, 6.NS.B.3, 6.NS.B.4

[3]These are terms and symbols students have seen previously.

EUREKA MATH

Mathematics Curriculum

6
GRADE

Topic A
Dividing Fractions by Fractions

6.NS.A.1

Focus Standard:	6.NS.A.1	Interpret and compute quotients of fractions, and solve word problems involving division of fractions by fractions, e.g., by using visual fraction models and equations to represent the problem. *For example, create a story context for (2/3) ÷ (3/4) and use a visual fraction model to show the quotient; use the relationship between multiplication and division to explain that (2/3) ÷ (3/4) = 8/9 because 3/4 of 8/9 is 2/3. (In general, (a/b) ÷ (c/d) = ad/bc). How much chocolate will each person get if 3 people share 1/2 lb. of chocolate equally? How many 3/4-cup servings are in 2/3 of a cup of yogurt? How wide is a rectangular strip of land with length 3/4 mi and area 1/2 square mi?*
Instructional Days:	8	
Lesson 1:	Interpreting Division of a Fraction by a Whole Number—Visual Models (P)[1]	
Lesson 2:	Interpreting Division of a Whole Number by a Fraction—Visual Models (P)	
Lessons 3–4:	Interpreting and Computing Division of a Fraction by a Fraction—More Models (P, P)	
Lesson 5:	Creating Division Stories (P)	
Lesson 6:	More Division Stories (P)	
Lesson 7:	The Relationship Between Visual Fraction Models and Equations (S)	
Lesson 8:	Dividing Fractions and Mixed Numbers (P)	

In Topic A, students extend their previous understanding of multiplication and division to divide fractions by fractions. Students determine quotients through visual models, such as bar diagrams, tape diagrams, arrays, and number line diagrams. They construct division stories and solve word problems involving division of fractions (**6.NS.A.1**). Students understand and apply partitive division of fractions to determine how much is in each group. They explore real-life situations that require them to ask themselves, "How much is one share?" and "What part of the unit is that share?" Students use measurement to determine quotients of fractions. They are presented conceptual problems where they determine that the quotient represents how many of the divisor is in the dividend. Students look for and uncover patterns while modeling quotients of fractions to ultimately discover the relationship between multiplication and division. Later in the module, students understand and apply the direct correlation of division of fractions to division of decimals.

---

[1]Lesson Structure Key: **P**-Problem Set Lesson, **M**-Modeling Cycle Lesson, **E**-Exploration Lesson, **S**-Socratic Lesson

---

Topic A: Dividing Fractions by Fractions

Lesson 1: Interpreting Division of a Fraction by a Whole Number—Visual Models

Student Outcomes

- Students use visual models, such as fraction bars, number lines, and area models, to show the quotient of whole numbers and fractions and to show the connection between them and the multiplication of fractions.
- Students divide a fraction by a whole number.

Classwork

Opening Exercise (5 minutes)

At the beginning of class, have students work in pairs to complete the following problems. Partner A completes the problems in column A, and Partner B completes the problems in column B.

Opening Exercise

A	**B**
Write a division sentence to solve each problem.	Write a multiplication sentence to solve each problem.
1. 8 gallons of batter are poured equally into 4 bowls. How many gallons of batter are in each bowl?	1. One fourth of an 8-gallon pail is poured out. How many gallons are poured out?
2. 1 gallon of batter is poured equally into 4 bowls. How many gallons of batter are in each bowl?	2. One fourth of a 1-gallon pail is poured out. How many gallons are poured out?
Write a division sentence *and* draw a model to solve.	Write a multiplication sentence *and* draw a model to solve.
3. 3 gallons of batter are poured equally into 4 bowls. How many gallons of batter are in each bowl?	3. One fourth of a 3-gallon pail is poured out. How many gallons are poured out?

After three minutes, have students share their division and multiplication sentences for each problem. Post the completed division and multiplication sentences alongside one another to allow for easy comparison. Have students discuss what they notice.

Emphasize the fact that dividing by 4 and multiplying by $\frac{1}{4}$ are equivalent. Use student models for Problem 3 to demonstrate this fact.

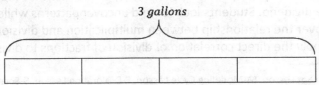

3 gallons

EUREKA MATH

Also, look for students who show work using unit language. For example in Problem 2 of column A, a student might recognize that in order to divide the gallon of batter equally among 4 bowls, it is helpful to think of 1 gallon as being equal to 4 fourths gallon (4 quarts). Likewise, in Problem 3 of column A, 3 gallons of batter is equal to 12 fourths gallons of batter.

⬚   2. $1 \div 4$

$4 \text{ fourths} \div 4 = 1 \text{ fourth} = \frac{1}{4}$

⬚   3. $3 \div 4$

$12 \text{ fourths} \div 4 = 3 \text{ fourths} = \frac{3}{4}$

To conclude the Opening Exercise, have students describe how their models would look if Problem 3 started with less than 1 gallon of batter being poured into 2 bowls.

Example 1 (7 minutes)

This lesson focuses on fractions divided by whole numbers. Students learned how to divide unit fractions by whole numbers in Grade 5. Teachers can become familiar with what was taught on this topic by reviewing the materials used in the Grade 5 Module 4 lessons and assessments.

Example 1

$\frac{3}{4}$ gallon of batter is poured equally into 2 bowls. How many gallons of batter are in each bowl?

■   Since the whole is being put into 2 equal parts or bowls, this is the partitive model of division. What division expression can we write to match this story?

⬚ $\frac{3}{4} \div 2$

■   We can also think of this problem as asking, "3 fourths is 2 groups of what?" Let's take a look at how to solve this using an area model. What is the whole? How much batter is being shared?

⬚   *Three-fourths gallon*

■   The story tells us that the batter is poured equally into 2 bowls. How can we show this in the model?

⬚   *We can draw another line, horizontally, to partition the model into 2 equal units.*

■   Now our model shows 3 fourths being partitioned into 2 equal parts. Could we also say that our model shows $\frac{1}{2}$ of 3 fourths?

⬚   *Yes, it's just like in the Opening Exercise where dividing by 2 and multiplying by $\frac{1}{2}$ are the same.*

■   Let's label our model to show that. What is half of 3 fourths?

⬚   *Half of 3 fourths is 3 eighths.*

■   Yes, and what is 3 fourths divided by 2?

⬚   *It's also 3 eighths!*

- We said that we could also think of this problem as, "3 fourths is 2 groups of what?" Is it true that 3 fourths is 2 groups of 3 eighths? Use a repeated addition or multiplication sentence to support your response.

  ▫ *Yes, it's true. 3 eighths plus 3 eighths is 6 eighths, which is equal to 3 fourths. → It's true.*

  $$2 \times \frac{3}{8} = \frac{6}{8} = \frac{3}{4}.$$

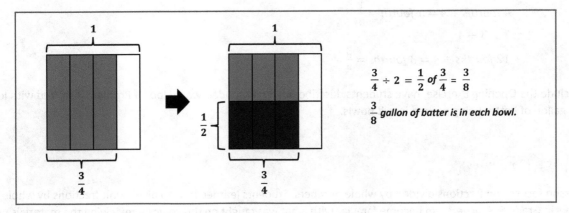

$$\frac{3}{4} \div 2 = \frac{1}{2} \text{ of } \frac{3}{4} = \frac{3}{8}$$

$\frac{3}{8}$ *gallon of batter is in each bowl.*

Example 2 (4 minutes)

> **Example 2**
>
> $\frac{3}{4}$ pan of lasagna is shared equally by 6 friends. What fraction of the pan will each friend get?

- Again, this is partitive division problem since we're told that there are 6 *parts*, or that the lasagna is being shared equally among 6 friends. Write a division expression to represent this story problem.

  ▫ $\frac{3}{4} \div 6$

- Remember when solving this problem, we can also think, "3 fourths is 6 groups of what?" Let's draw another area model to solve. Think, what is our whole? Draw a model to show how much lasagna is being shared.

- Now, partition your model again to show how it can be equally shared by 6 friends.

- Remind me; dividing by 6 is the same as multiplying by what?

  ▫ *Multiplying by $\frac{1}{6}$*

- Look at our model. Explain to your neighbor how it shows division by 6 and also shows multiplication by $\frac{1}{6}$.

- Now write a multiplication expression that is equal to 3 fourths divided by 6.

  ▫ $\frac{1}{6} \text{ of } \frac{3}{4} \text{ or } \frac{1}{6} \times \frac{3}{4}$

Lesson 1:   Interpreting Division of a Fraction by a Whole Number—Visual Models

$$\frac{3}{4} \div 6 = \frac{1}{6} \ of \ \frac{3}{4} = \frac{3}{24} = \frac{1}{8}$$

- According to our model, what fraction of the pan will each friend get?

   □   3 *twenty-fourths of the pan*

- Express 3 twenty-fourths in its simplest form.

   □   1 *eighth*

Example 3 (5 minutes)

> **Example 3**
>
> A rope of length $\frac{2}{5}$ m is cut into 4 equal cords. What is the length of each cord?

- Again, this is a partitive division problem since we're told that there are 4 *parts* or that the rope is cut equally into 4 cords. Write a division expression to represent this story problem.

   □ $\frac{2}{5} \div 4$

- For this example, let's draw a tape diagram and a number line.

- The length of rope is cut into 4 equal cords. How can we show that in our models?

   □   *Partition the 2 shaded units into 4 equal parts.*

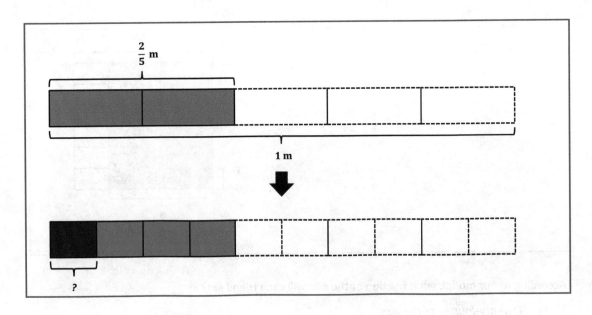

- We originally drew fifths and shaded 2 of them to represent the length of the rope, but now what fractional unit does our model show?
  - *Tenths*
- Answer the question. What is the length of each cord?
  - *Each cord is $\frac{1}{10}$ meter long.*

$\frac{2}{5} \div 4 = \frac{1}{4}$ of $\frac{2}{5} = \frac{2}{20} = \frac{1}{10}$

Each cord is $\frac{1}{10}$ m.

$\frac{2}{5} \div 4 = 4$ tenths $\div 4 = 1$ tenth $= \frac{1}{10}$

- Take a look at the division sentence I've written using unit language. How do our models support this thought? How does the use of unit language support your understanding of this division problem?
- We can also construct a number line to support our solution. When the number line is drawn beneath the tape diagram, we can see the similarities between the two models.

EUREKA MATH

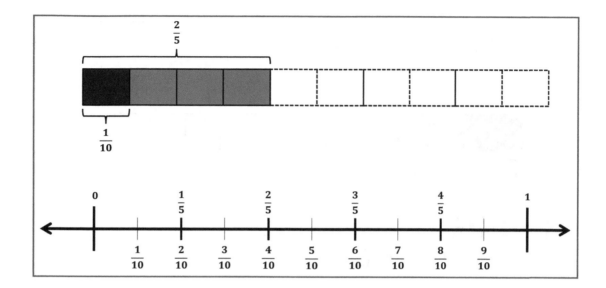

Encourage students to study the models and discuss the similarities between dividing by 4 and multiplying by $\frac{1}{4}$. Students should articulate that both operations yield the same result.

Exercises 1–6 (14 minutes)

Students work in pairs to solve the following questions.

Exercises 1–6

Fill in the blank to complete the equation. Then, find the quotient and draw a model to support your solution.

1. $\frac{1}{2} \div 3 = \frac{\square}{3} \times \frac{1}{2}$

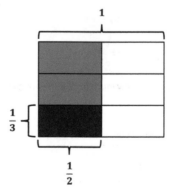

$$\frac{1}{2} \div 3 = \frac{1}{3} \times \frac{1}{2} = \frac{1}{6}$$

2. $\frac{1}{3} \div 4 = \frac{1}{4} \times \frac{1}{\square}$

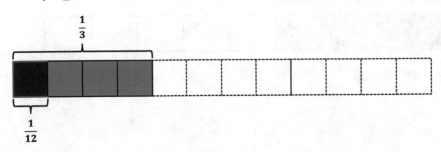

$\frac{1}{3} \div 4 = \frac{1}{4} \times \frac{1}{3} = \frac{1}{12}$

$\frac{1}{3} \div 4 = 4 \text{ tweflths} \div 4 = 1 \text{ tweflth} = \frac{1}{12}$

Find the value of each of the following.

3. $\frac{1}{4} \div 5$

$\frac{1}{4} \div 5 = \frac{1}{5} \text{ of } \frac{1}{4} = \frac{1}{20}$

4. $\frac{3}{4} \div 5$

$\frac{3}{4} \div 5 = \frac{1}{5} \text{ of } \frac{3}{4} = \frac{3}{20}$

5. $\frac{1}{5} \div 4$

$\frac{1}{5} \div 4 = \frac{1}{4} \text{ of } \frac{1}{5} = \frac{1}{20}$

Solve. Draw a model to support your solution.

6. $\frac{3}{5}$ pt. of juice is poured equally into 6 glasses. How much juice is in each glass?

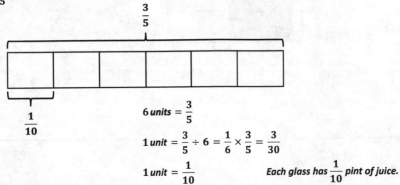

6 units $= \frac{3}{5}$

1 unit $= \frac{3}{5} \div 6 = \frac{1}{6} \times \frac{3}{5} = \frac{3}{30}$

1 unit $= \frac{1}{10}$ *Each glass has $\frac{1}{10}$ pint of juice.*

EUREKA MATH

Exit Ticket Sample Solutions

Write an equivalent multiplication expression. Then, find the quotient in its simplest form. Use a model to support your response.

1. $\dfrac{1}{4} \div 2$

$$\dfrac{1}{4} \div 2 = \dfrac{1}{2} \times \dfrac{1}{4} = \dfrac{1}{8}$$

2. $\dfrac{2}{3} \div 6$

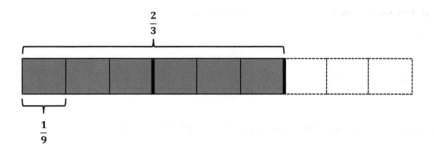

$$\dfrac{2}{3} \div 6 = \dfrac{1}{6} \times \dfrac{2}{3} = \dfrac{2}{18} = \dfrac{1}{9}$$

Problem Set Solutions

Find the value of each of the following in its simplest form.

1.

   a. $\dfrac{1}{3} \div 4 = \dfrac{1}{12}$ b. $\dfrac{2}{5} \div 4 = \dfrac{1}{10}$ c. $\dfrac{4}{7} \div 4 = \dfrac{1}{7}$

2.

   a. $\dfrac{2}{5} \div 3 = \dfrac{2}{15}$ b. $\dfrac{5}{6} \div 5 = \dfrac{1}{6}$ c. $\dfrac{5}{8} \div 10 = \dfrac{1}{16}$

3.

   a. $\dfrac{6}{7} \div 3 = \dfrac{2}{7}$ b. $\dfrac{10}{8} \div 5 = \dfrac{1}{4}$ c. $\dfrac{20}{6} \div 2 = \dfrac{5}{3}$

4. 4 loads of stone weigh $\dfrac{2}{3}$ ton. Find the weight of 1 load of stone.

$$\dfrac{2}{3} \div 4 = \dfrac{1}{6}$$

Each load of stone weighs $\dfrac{1}{6}$ ton.

5. What is the width of a rectangle with an area of $\dfrac{5}{8}$ in² and a length of 10 inches?

$$\dfrac{5}{8} \div 10 = \dfrac{1}{16}$$

The width of the rectangle is $\dfrac{1}{16}$ in.

6. Lenox ironed $\dfrac{1}{4}$ of the shirts over the weekend. She plans to split the remainder of the work equally over the next 5 evenings.

   a. What fraction of the shirts will Lenox iron each day after school?

$$\dfrac{3}{4} \div 5 = \dfrac{3}{20}$$

Lenox will iron $\dfrac{3}{20}$ of the shirts each day after school.

   b. If Lenox has 40 shirts, how many shirts will she need to iron on Thursday and Friday?

$$\dfrac{3}{20}(40) = 6$$

Lenox will need to iron 6 shirts on Thursday and 6 shirts on Friday.

Therefore, Lenox will need to iron 12 shirts on Thursday and Friday.

EUREKA MATH

7. Bo paid bills with $\frac{1}{2}$ of his paycheck and put $\frac{1}{5}$ of the remainder in savings. The rest of his paycheck he divided equally among the college accounts of his 3 children.

a. What fraction of his paycheck went into each child's account?

$\frac{1}{2}\left(\frac{1}{5}\right) = \frac{1}{10}$. *This means* $\frac{1}{10}$ *of Bo's paycheck goes into savings.* $\frac{1}{2} + \frac{1}{10} = \frac{5}{10} + \frac{1}{10} = \frac{6}{10} = \frac{3}{5}$.

This means that $\frac{3}{5}$ *of Bo's paycheck goes to bills and savings, which leaves* $\frac{2}{5}$ *of his paycheck for college accounts.*

$\frac{2}{5} \div 3 = \frac{2}{15}$

Therefore, Bo put $\frac{2}{15}$ *of his paycheck in each child's account.*

b. If Bo deposited $400 in each child's account, how much money was in Bo's original paycheck?

$400 \text{ is } \frac{2}{15}$ *group of what size?*

2 *units* $= \$400$
1 *unit* $= \$400 \div 2 = \$200$
15 *units* $= 15 \times \$200 = \$3,000$ *Bo was originally paid* $\$3,000$.

Lesson 2: Interpreting Division of a Whole Number by a Fraction—Visual Models

Student Outcomes

- Students use fraction bars, number lines, and area models to show the quotient of whole numbers and fractions and to show the connection between those models and the multiplication of fractions.
- Students understand the difference between a whole number being divided by a fraction and a fraction being divided by a whole number.

Classwork

Example 1 (15 minutes)

At the beginning of class, break students into groups. Each group needs to answer the question they have been assigned and draw a model to represent their answer. Multiple groups could have the same question.

Group 1: How many half miles are in 12 miles? $12 \div \frac{1}{2} = 24$

Group 2: How many quarter hours are in 5 hours? $5 \div \frac{1}{4} = 20$

Group 3: How many one-third cups are in 9 cups? $9 \div \frac{1}{3} = 27$

Group 4: How many one-eighth pizzas are in 4 pizzas? $4 \div \frac{1}{8} = 32$

Group 5: How many one-fifths are in 7 wholes? $7 \div \frac{1}{5} = 35$

MP.1 & MP.2

Models will vary but could include tape diagrams, number lines, or area models (arrays).

Students draw models on blank paper, construction paper, or chart paper. Hang up only student models, and have students travel around the room answering the following:

1. Write the division expression that this model represents.
2. Write a multiplication expression that this model could also represent.
3. Write an equation showing the equivalence of the two expressions.

Students are given a table to fill in as they visit each model.

When discussing the opening of this example, ask students how these problems are different from those solved in Lesson 1. Students should notice that these questions are dividing whole numbers by fractions, while the questions in Lesson 1 were dividing fractions by whole numbers.

Discuss how the division and multiplication expressions are related. Students should recognize that when 12 is divided into halves, it is the same as doubling 12.

EUREKA MATH

Example 1

Question # _____

Write it as a division expression.   _____

Write it as a multiplication expression.   _____

Make a rough draft of a model to represent the problem:

As you travel to each model, be sure to answer the following questions:

Original Question	Corresponding Division Expression	Corresponding Multiplication Expression	Write an Equation Showing the Equivalence of the Two Expressions.
1. How many $\frac{1}{2}$ miles are in 12 miles?	$12 \div \frac{1}{2}$	12×2	$12 \div \frac{1}{2} = 12 \times 2$
2. How many quarter hours are in 5 hours?	$5 \div \frac{1}{4}$	5×4	$5 \div \frac{1}{4} = 5 \times 4$
3. How many $\frac{1}{3}$ cups are in 9 cups?	$9 \div \frac{1}{3}$	9×3	$9 \div \frac{1}{3} = 9 \times 3$
4. How many $\frac{1}{8}$ pizzas are in 4 pizzas?	$4 \div \frac{1}{8}$	4×8	$4 \div \frac{1}{8} = 4 \times 8$
5. How many one-fifths are in 7 wholes?	$7 \div \frac{1}{5}$	7×5	$7 \div \frac{1}{5} = 7 \times 5$

Example 2 (5 minutes)

- All of the problems in the first example show what is called *measurement division*. In measurement division, the divisor names the size (or measure) of the group (or unit), and the quotient represents the number of groups (or units). A measurement division problem can often be solved by thinking, "How many _____ are in _____?"

- Let's take a look at a different example:

Example 2

Molly has 9 cups of flour. If this is $\frac{3}{4}$ of the amount she needs to make bread, how many cups does she need?

Post the interpretive question, "9 is $\frac{3}{4}$ group of what size?"

> **a.** **Construct the tape diagram by reading it backward. Draw a tape diagram and label the unknown.**
>
> ?
>
> **b.** **Next, shade in $\frac{3}{4}$**
>
>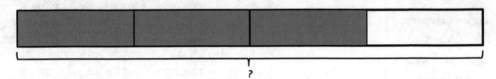
>
> ?
>
> **c.** **Label the shaded region to show that 9 is equal to $\frac{3}{4}$ of the total.**
>
> 9
>
>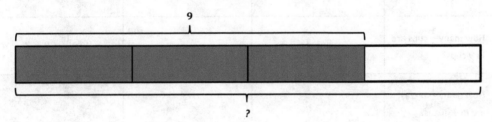
>
> ?
>
> **d.** **Analyze the model to determine the quotient.**
>
> **3** *units* = 9
>
> **1** *unit* = 9 ÷ 3 = 3
>
> **4** *units* = 4 × 3 = 12   *Molly needs* 12 *cups of flour to make bread.*

- Can we interpret this problem using division?

  ▫ *In the problem we knew that 9 is $\frac{3}{4}$ of something. So it's like multiplication:* $9 = \frac{3}{4} \times$ _____. *To find what goes in the blank, we divide:* $9 \div \frac{3}{4}$.

EUREKA
MATH

■   How is this question different from the measurement division questions?

▫   *In this partitive division word problem, represented by the expression $9 \div \frac{3}{4}$, the divisor represents the **number of groups** (in this case 3 fourths of a group), and the quotient tells the **size of the group**. In a partitive division expression using whole numbers, like $24 \div 6$ (where 6 represents the number of groups), a student might think, "24 is 6 groups of what size?" In this example, the story context tells us that 9 cups is 3 fourths of a group. Encourage the thinking, "9 is $\frac{3}{4}$ group of what size?"*

Exercises 1–5 (15 minutes)

Students work in pairs or on their own to solve the following questions. First, students write a division expression to represent the problem. Then, students write an interpretive question to guide their thinking. Finally, they draw a model to represent the solution.

Allow time for students to share their models. Take time to have students compare the different models that were used to solve each question. For example, allow students to see how a tape diagram and a number line can be used to model Exercise 1.

Exercises 1–5

1. A construction company is setting up signs on 2 miles of a road. If the company places a sign at every $\frac{1}{4}$ mile, how many signs will it use?

$2 \div \frac{1}{4} \rightarrow$ *How many* $\frac{1}{4}$ *in 2?*

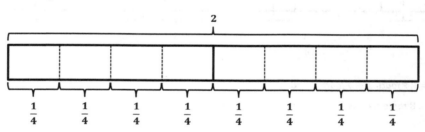

$2 \div \frac{1}{4} = 8 \ fourths \div 1 \ fourth = 8$

There are 8 fourths in 2. The company will use 8 signs.

---

2. George bought 4 submarine sandwiches for a birthday party. If each person will eat $\frac{2}{3}$ of a sandwich, how many people can George feed?

$4 \div \frac{2}{3} \rightarrow$ How many $\frac{2}{3}$ in 4?

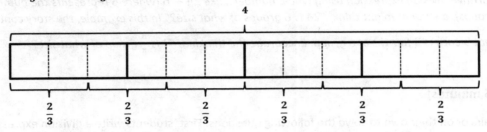

$4 \div \frac{2}{3} = 12$ *thirds* $\div 2$ *thirds* $= 6$

There are 6 two-thirds in 4. George can feed 6 people.

3. Miranda buys 6 pounds of nuts. If she puts $\frac{3}{4}$ pound in each bag, how many bags can she make?

$6 \div \frac{3}{4} \rightarrow$ How many $\frac{3}{4}$ in 6?

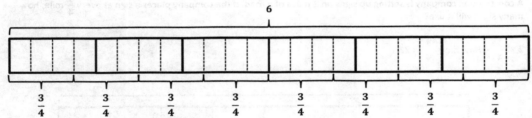

$6 \div \frac{3}{4} = 24$ *fourths* $\div 3$ *fourths* $= 8$

There are 8 three-fourths in 6. Miranda can make 8 bags.

4. Margo freezes 8 cups of strawberries. If this is $\frac{2}{3}$ of the total strawberries that she picked, how many cups of strawberries did Margo pick?

$8 \div \frac{2}{3} \rightarrow 8$ is $\frac{2}{3}$ group of what size?

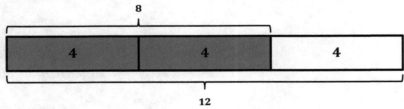

2 *units* $= 8$

1 *unit* $= 8 \div 2 = 4$

3 *units* $= 3 \times 4 = 12$ **Margo picked 12 cups of strawberries.**

EUREKA
MATH

5. Regina is chopping up wood. She has chopped 10 logs so far. If the 10 logs represent $\frac{5}{8}$ of all the logs that need to be chopped, how many logs need to be chopped in all?

$10 \div \frac{5}{8} \rightarrow 10$ *is* $\frac{5}{8}$ *group of what size?*

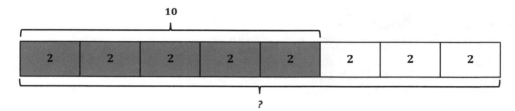

5 *units* = 10

1 *unit* = 10 ÷ 5 = 2

8 *units* = 8 × 2 = 16   *Regina will chop* 16 *logs.*

Closing (5 minutes)

- What are the key ideas from Lessons 1 and 2?
  - *We can use models to divide a whole number by a fraction and a fraction by a whole number.*
- When you solved $6 \div \frac{3}{4}$ using measurement division, how was that like multiplying $6 \times \frac{4}{3}$?
  - *When we divided, we changed 6 into 6 × 4 fourths, or 24 fourths, and then we divided 24 fourths ÷ 3 fourths to get 8. When you multiply 6 by $\frac{4}{3}$, you do the same thing—multiply 6 by 4, and then divide by 3. So they are exactly the same.*
- When you solved $8 \div \frac{2}{3}$ using partitive division, how was that like multiplying $8 \times \frac{3}{2}$?
  - *Our diagram showed that we could divide 8 by 2 to get 1 unit = 4. Since we had 3 units in the whole, we multiplied 4 by 3 to get 12. When we multiply 8 and $\frac{3}{2}$, you can do the same thing since $\frac{3}{2} = \left(\frac{1}{2}\right) \times 3$: multiply 8 by $\frac{1}{2}$ first, and then multiply the result by 3. So they are exactly the same.*

Exit Ticket (5 minutes)

Lesson 2:   Interpreting Division of a Whole Number by a Fraction—Visual Models

27

Name _____   Date _____

Lesson 2: Interpreting Division of a Whole Number by a Fraction—Visual Models

Exit Ticket

Solve each division problem using a model.

1.   Henry bought 4 pies, which he plans to share with a group of his friends. If there is exactly enough to give each member of the group one-sixth of the pie, how many people are in the group?

2.   Rachel finished $\frac{3}{4}$ of the race in 6 hours. How long was the entire race?

Exit Ticket Sample Solutions

Solve each division problem using a model.

1. Henry bought 4 pies, which he plans to share with a group of his friends. If there is exactly enough to give each member of the group one-sixth of the pie, how many people are in the group?

   $4 \div \dfrac{1}{6} \rightarrow$ *How many* $\dfrac{1}{6}$ *in 4?*

   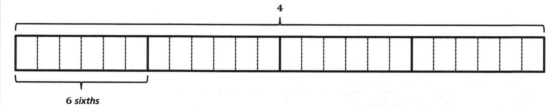

   There are 6 sixths in 1, and 24 sixths in 4. Henry can share the pies with 24 people.

2. Rachel finished $\dfrac{3}{4}$ of the race in 6 hours. How long was the entire race?

   $6 \div \dfrac{3}{4} \rightarrow \dfrac{3}{4}$ *of what number is 6?*

   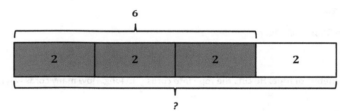

   3 units = 6

   1 units = 6 ÷ 3 = 2

   4 units = 4 × 2 = 8

   The race was 8 hours.

Problem Set Sample Solutions

Rewrite each problem as a multiplication question. Model your answer.

1. Nicole used $\frac{3}{8}$ of her ribbon to wrap a present. If she used 6 feet of ribbon for the present, how much ribbon did Nicole have at first?

$6 \div \frac{3}{8}$

6 is $\frac{3}{8}$ of what number?

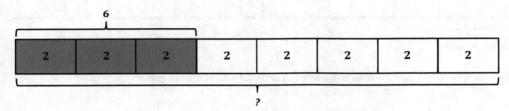

3 *units* = 6

1 *unit* = 6 ÷ 3 = 2

8 *units* = 8 × 2 = 16

Nicole started with 16 *feet of ribbon.*

2. A Boy Scout has 3 meters of rope. He cuts the rope into cords $\frac{3}{5}$ m long. How many cords will he make?

How many $\frac{3}{5}$ *are in 3?*

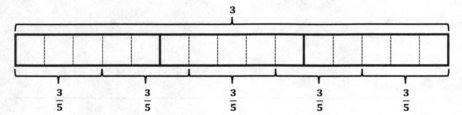

$3 \div \frac{3}{5} = 15\ fifths \div 3\ fifths = \frac{15}{3} = 5$

The Boy Scout can make 5 *cords.*

3. 12 gallons of water fill a tank to $\frac{3}{4}$ capacity.

    a. **What is the capacity of the tank?**

    $12 \div \frac{3}{4}$

    12 is $\frac{3}{4}$ of what number?

    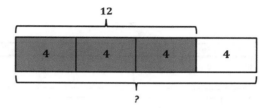

    3 units = 12

    1 unit = 12 ÷ 3 = 4

    4 units = 4 × 4 = 16

    The tank's capacity is 16 gallons.

    b. **If the tank is then filled to capacity, how many half-gallon bottles can be filled with the water in the tank?**

    How many $\frac{1}{2}$ are in 16?

    $16 \div \frac{1}{2}$ 32 halves ÷ 1 half = 32

    32 bottles can be filled.

4. Hunter spent $\frac{2}{3}$ of his money on a video game before spending half of his remaining money on lunch. If his lunch costs \$10, how much money did he have at first?

    \$10 is $\frac{1}{6}$ of what number?

    $10 \div \frac{1}{6}$

    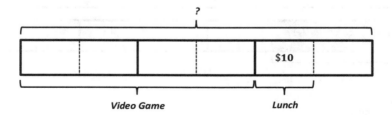

    1 unit = \$10

    6 units = 6 × \$10 = \$60

    Hunter had \$60 at first.

5. Students were surveyed about their favorite colors. $\frac{1}{4}$ of the students preferred red, $\frac{1}{8}$ of the students preferred blue, and $\frac{3}{5}$ of the remaining students preferred green. If 15 students preferred green, how many students were surveyed?

15 is $\frac{3}{8}$ of what number?

$15 \div \frac{3}{8}$

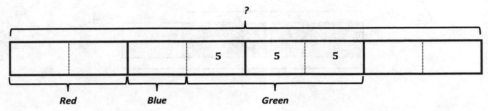

3 units = 15

1 unit = 15 ÷ 3 = 5

8 units = 8 × 5 = 40

40 students were surveyed.

6. Mr. Scruggs got some money for his birthday. He spent $\frac{1}{5}$ of it on dog treats. Then, he divided the remainder equally among his 3 favorite charities.

a. What fraction of his money did each charity receive?

   $\frac{4}{5} \div 3 = \frac{1}{3} \times \frac{4}{5} = \frac{4}{15}$ *Each charity received $\frac{4}{15}$ of Mr. Scruggs' birthday money.*

b. If he donated $60 to each charity, how much money did he receive for his birthday?

   60 is $\frac{4}{15}$ of what number?

   $60 \div \frac{4}{15}$

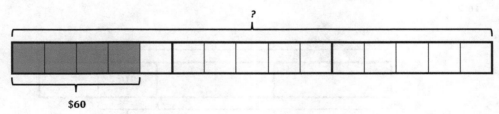

4 units = $60

1 unit = $60 ÷ 4 = $15

15 units = 15 × $15 = $225

Mr. Scruggs got $225 for his birthday.

Lesson 2:   Interpreting Division of a Whole Number by a Fraction—Visual Models

EUREKA MATH®

Lesson 3: Interpreting and Computing Division of a Fraction by a Fraction—More Models

Student Outcomes

- Students use fraction bars and area models to show the division of fractions by fractions with common denominators.
- Students make connections to the multiplication of fractions. In addition, students understand that to get the quotient when dividing fractions, they must ask, "How many groups of the divisor are in the dividend?"

Classwork

Opening Exercise (5 minutes)

Begin class with a review of how to divide a whole number by a whole number using a model.

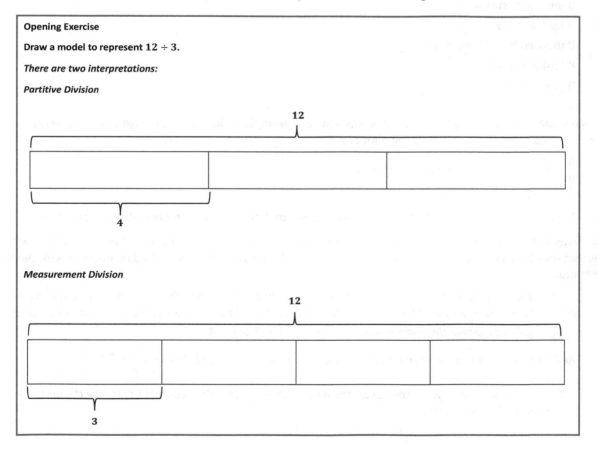

Opening Exercise

Draw a model to represent $12 \div 3$.

There are two interpretations:

Partitive Division

12

4

Measurement Division

12

3

Create a question or word problem that matches your model.

Answers will vary.

Sample Solutions for Partitive Division Model:

12 cards are shared with 3 people. How many cards does each person get?

12 is 3 of what number?

Sample Solutions for Measurement Division Model:

12 balls are put in groups of 3. How many groups are made?

How many 3's are in 12?

Example 1 (5 minutes)

Next, an example is introduced where students are asked to divide a fraction by a fraction with the same denominator. In order to allow students to appreciate the simplicity in dividing with like units, have students find the quotient for each example in the sequence below.

- $8 \div 2 =$ ____
- 8 ones ÷ 2 ones = ____
- 8 tens ÷ 2 tens = ____
- 8 thousands ÷ 2 thousands = ____
- 8 tenths ÷ 2 tenths = ____
- 8 thirds ÷ 2 thirds = ____

Encourage students to discuss why the quotient was 4 in each example. Help students recognize that since the units are the same, the basic fact $8 \div 4 = 2$ gives the quotient.

- $\frac{8}{9} \div \frac{2}{9}$ Write this expression in unit form.
  - 8 ninths ÷ 2 ninths

MP.1

- Take a moment to use what you know about division to draw a model to represent this expression.

Give students a chance to explore this question and draw models. After three minutes or so, ask students to share the models that they have created and to discuss what conclusions they have made about dividing fractions with the same denominator.

  - *We can ask, "8 ninths is how many 2 ninths?" Since the units are the same, that's just like asking, "How many 2's are in 8?" From the model, I can see that there are 4 groups of 2 ninths in 8 ninths. This would give the same solution as dividing 8 by 2 to get 4.*

- Reflect on the pattern you saw in Lesson 2. Does that pattern still apply here? Is $\frac{8}{9} \div \frac{2}{9} = \frac{8}{9} \times \frac{9}{2}$?

  - *When we multiply, we can cancel the nines and get $\frac{8}{2}$. The nines cancel out just like the ninths canceled out when we divided!*

Lesson 3: Interpreting and Computing Division of a Fraction by a Fraction—More Models

Example 1

$$\frac{8}{9} \div \frac{2}{9}$$

Write the expression in unit form, and then draw a model to solve.

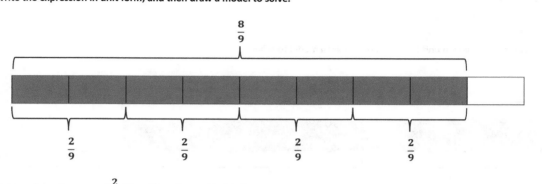

Here we have 4 groups of $\frac{2}{9}$. Therefore, the quotient is 4.

Example 2 (5 minutes)

■ $\frac{9}{12} \div \frac{3}{12}$ Write the expression in unit form, and then draw a model to solve.

□ *One way to interpret this question is by saying, "How many $\frac{3}{12}$ are in $\frac{9}{12}$?" In other words, I need to divide 9 twelfths by 3 twelfths, which is the same as $9 \div 3$, which is 3.*

Example 2

$$\frac{9}{12} \div \frac{3}{12}$$

Write the expression in unit form, and then draw a model to solve.

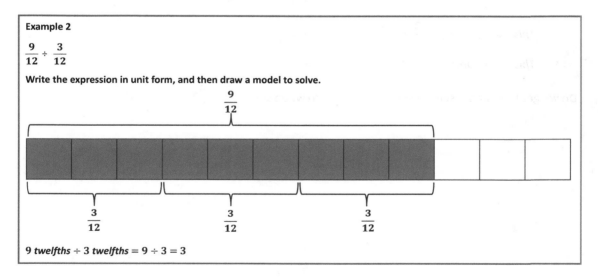

9 *twelfths* ÷ 3 *twelfths* = 9 ÷ 3 = 3

Have students discuss if solving $\frac{9}{12} \div \frac{3}{12}$ is the same as $\frac{9}{12} \times \frac{12}{3}$.

Example 3 (3 minutes)

Example 3

$$\frac{7}{9} \div \frac{3}{9}$$

Write the expression in unit form, and then draw a model to solve.

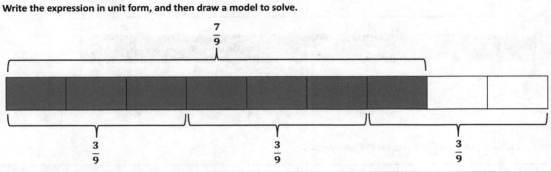

- Look at your model. How many units of $\frac{3}{9}$ can you see in $\frac{7}{9}$?

  □ 2 *complete units and then part of another*

- How can we name the part of the incomplete unit?

  □ *There is one out of the three needed pieces to make another whole. So, it is* $2\frac{1}{3}$.

  □ *This means that* $\frac{7}{9} \div \frac{3}{9} = 2\frac{1}{3}$.

  □ *This is the same as* $7 \div 3$.

- Do we get the same result solving $\frac{7}{9} \div \frac{3}{9}$ as we do when solving $\frac{7}{9} \times \frac{9}{3}$?

Interpreting and Computing Division of a Fraction by a Fraction—More
Models

EUREKA
MATH

Exercises 1–6 (17 minutes)

Students work in pairs or alone to solve more questions about division with like denominators.

Exercises 1–6

Write an expression to represent each problem. Then, draw a model to solve.

1. **How many fourths are in 3 fourths?**

    I need to divide three fourths by one fourth, which is 3.

    $$\frac{3}{4} \div \frac{1}{4} = 3 \text{ fourths} \div 1 \text{ fourth} = 3 \div 1$$

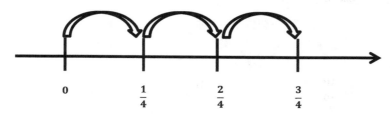

    There are 3 one-fourths in three-fourths.

2. $\frac{4}{5} \div \frac{2}{5}$

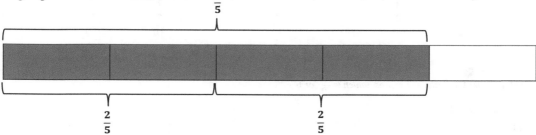

    This is really 4 fifths ÷ 2 fifths, which is 2.

3. $\frac{9}{4} \div \frac{3}{4}$

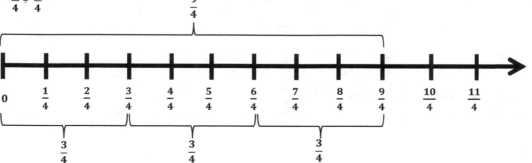

    This is really 9 fourths ÷ 3 fourths, which is 3.

4. $\dfrac{7}{8} \div \dfrac{2}{8}$

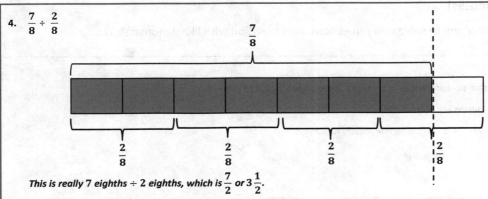

This is really 7 eighths ÷ 2 eighths, which is $\dfrac{7}{2}$ or $3\dfrac{1}{2}$.

5. $\dfrac{13}{10} \div \dfrac{2}{10}$

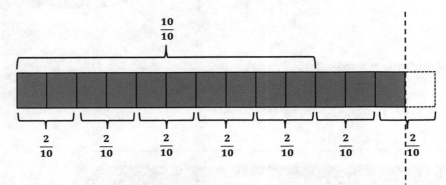

This is really 13 tenths ÷ 2 tenths, which is $\dfrac{13}{2}$ or $6\dfrac{1}{2}$.

6. $\dfrac{11}{9} \div \dfrac{3}{9}$

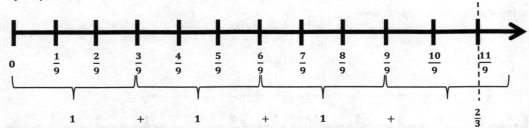

This is really 11 ninths ÷ 3 ninths, which is $\dfrac{11}{3}$ or $3\dfrac{2}{3}$.

Lesson 3:   Interpreting and Computing Division of a Fraction by a Fraction—More Models

EUREKA MATH

Closing (5 minutes)

Depending on how much time there is in the class, have each student write to another student an actual note that contains models and a description of the ideas discussed in class. Or, if time is short, this can be a discussion.

- Imagine that your best friend missed today's lesson. What key ideas would you want your friend to know in order to be able to divide fractions by fractions with the same denominator?

  □ *When dividing with like units, you can just divide the numerators and think of basic facts. For example,* 8 cm ÷ 2 cm = 4, *just like* 8 *ninths* ÷ 2 *ninths* = 4.

  □ *We can use a variety of models to show that when dividing fractions by fractions with the same denominator, it is equivalent to dividing the numerators.*

- Make a prediction. Will the rule given in the Lesson Summary apply to partitive division problems as well?

  □ *Answers may vary. This rule will apply to partitive division problems.*

Lesson Summary

When dividing a fraction by a fraction with the same denominator, we can use the general rule $\frac{a}{c} \div \frac{b}{c} = \frac{a}{b}$.

Exit Ticket (5 minutes)

Name _____   Date _____

Lesson 3: Interpreting and Computing Division of a Fraction by a Fraction—More Models

Exit Ticket

Find the quotient. Draw a model to support your solution.

1. $\dfrac{9}{4} \div \dfrac{3}{4}$

2. $\dfrac{7}{3} \div \dfrac{2}{3}$

Lesson 3:   Interpreting and Computing Division of a Fraction by a Fraction—More Models

© 2015 Great Minds. eureka-math.org
G6-M2-TE-B2-1.3.1-01.2016

EUREKA MATH

Exit Ticket Sample Solutions

Find the quotient. Draw a model to support your solution.

1. $\dfrac{9}{4} \div \dfrac{3}{4}$

    This is really 9 fourths ÷ 3 fourths, which is 3.

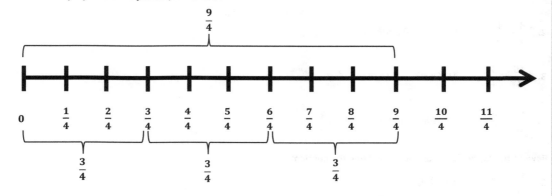

2. $\dfrac{7}{3} \div \dfrac{2}{3}$

    This is really 7 thirds ÷ 2 thirds, which is $\dfrac{7}{2}$ or $3\dfrac{1}{2}$.

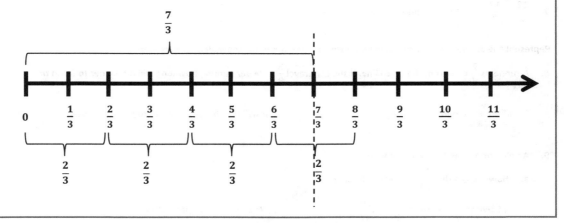

Problem Set Solutions

For the following exercises, rewrite the division expression in unit form. Then, find the quotient. Draw a model to support your answer.

1. $\dfrac{4}{5} \div \dfrac{1}{5}$ 4 *fifths* ÷ 1 *fifth* = 4

2. $\dfrac{8}{9} \div \dfrac{4}{9}$ 8 *ninths* ÷ 4 *ninths* = 2

3. $\dfrac{15}{4} \div \dfrac{3}{4}$ 15 *fourths* ÷ 3 *fourths* = 5

4. $\dfrac{13}{5} \div \dfrac{4}{5}$ 13 *fifths* ÷ 4 *fifths* = $\dfrac{13}{4}$ = $3\dfrac{1}{4}$

Rewrite the expression in unit form, and find the quotient.

5. $\dfrac{10}{3} \div \dfrac{2}{3}$ 10 *thirds* ÷ 2 *thirds* = 5

6. $\dfrac{8}{5} \div \dfrac{3}{5}$ 8 *fifths* ÷ 3 *fifths* = $\dfrac{8}{3}$ = $2\dfrac{2}{3}$

7. $\dfrac{12}{7} \div \dfrac{12}{7}$ 12 *sevenths* ÷ 12 *sevenths* = 1

Represent the division expression using unit form. Find the quotient. Show all necessary work.

8. A runner is $\dfrac{7}{8}$ mile from the finish line. If she can travel $\dfrac{3}{8}$ mile per minute, how long will it take her to finish the race?

7 *eighths* ÷ 3 *eighths* = $\dfrac{7}{3}$ = $2\dfrac{1}{3}$ *It will take her* $2\dfrac{1}{3}$ *minutes to finish the race.*

9. An electrician has 4.1 meters of wire.

    a. How many strips $\dfrac{7}{10}$ m long can he cut?

       41 *tenths* ÷ 7 *tenths* = $\dfrac{41}{7}$ = $5\dfrac{6}{7}$ *He can cut* 5 *complete strips.*

    b. How much wire will he have left over?

       He will have $\dfrac{6}{10}$ m *left over.*

© 2015 Great Minds. eureka-math.org
G6-M2-TE-B2-1.3.1-01.2016

EUREKA MATH

10. Saeed bought $21\frac{1}{2}$ lb. of ground beef. He used $\frac{1}{4}$ of the beef to make tacos and $\frac{2}{3}$ of the remainder to make quarter-pound burgers. How many burgers did he make?

   $\frac{1}{2}$ *of* $21\frac{1}{2}$ $= 10\frac{3}{4} \rightarrow 10\frac{3}{4}$ lb. *of beef is used for burgers.*

   43 *fourths* $\div 1$ *fourth* $= 43$ ***Saeed made*** 43 ***burgers.***

11. A baker bought some flour. He used $\frac{2}{5}$ of the flour to make bread and used the rest to make batches of muffins. If he used 16 lb. of flour making bread and $\frac{2}{3}$ lb. for each batch of muffins, how many batches of muffins did he make?

   16 *is* $\frac{2}{5}$ *group of what size?* $24 \div \frac{2}{3}$

   2 *units* $= 16$

   1 *unit* $= 16 \div 2 = 8$ 72 *thirds* $\div 2$ *thirds* $= 36$

   3 *units* $= 3 \times 8 = 24$ ***The baker made*** 36 ***batches of muffins.***

   The baker used 24 lb. ***of flour for muffins.***

Lesson 4: Interpreting and Computing Division of a Fraction by a Fraction—More Models

Student Outcomes

- Students use fraction bars and area models to divide fractions by fractions with different denominators.
- Students make connections between visual models and multiplication of fractions.

Classwork

Opening Exercise (2 minutes)

Begin class with a review of equivalent fractions. Ask each student for a new example of an equivalent fraction. Students need to share how they know that the new fraction is equivalent to the old fraction.

Opening Exercise

Write at least three equivalent fractions for each fraction below.

a. $\dfrac{2}{3}$

  Sample solutions include $\dfrac{4}{6}, \dfrac{6}{9}, \dfrac{8}{12}, \dfrac{10}{15}, \dfrac{12}{18}$

b. $\dfrac{10}{12}$

  Sample solutions include $\dfrac{5}{6}, \dfrac{15}{18}, \dfrac{20}{24}, \dfrac{25}{30}, \dfrac{30}{36}$

Example 1 (Optional)

This example is a review of the problems completed in the previous lesson. Therefore, it is decided by the teacher if this example is necessary or not.

For the first example, students are asked to solve a word problem using the skills they used in Lesson 3 to divide fractions with the same denominator.

MP.1

- Molly has $1\dfrac{3}{8}$ cups of strawberries. This can also be represented as $\dfrac{11}{8}$. She needs $\dfrac{3}{8}$ cup of strawberries to make one batch of muffins. How many batches can Molly make?

  - *This question is really asking me how many $\dfrac{3}{8}$ are in $\dfrac{11}{8}$ or, in other words, to divide 11 eighths by 3 eighths. I can use a model to show that there are enough strawberries to make $3\dfrac{2}{3}$ batches of muffins.*

EUREKA
MATH

Example 1

Molly has $1\frac{3}{8}$ cups of strawberries. She needs $\frac{3}{8}$ cup of strawberries to make one batch of muffins. How many batches can Molly make?

Use a model to support your answer.

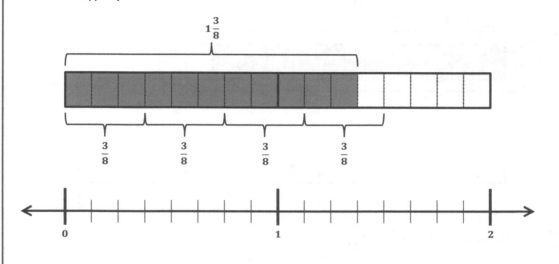

MP.1

$\frac{11}{8} \div \frac{3}{8} = 11$ *eighths* ÷ 3 *eighths* $= \frac{11}{3} = 3\frac{2}{3}$

Molly can make $3\frac{2}{3}$ *batches of muffins.*

Example 2 (3 minutes)

- Molly's friend, Xavier, also has $\frac{11}{8}$ cups of strawberries. He needs $\frac{3}{4}$ cup strawberries to make a batch of tarts. How many batches can he make?

  - *He has purchased $\frac{11}{8}$ cups, which makes* 1 *and* $\frac{5}{6}$ *batches.* (This would be answered last after a brief discussion using the questions that follow.)

- What is this question asking us to do?

  - *I am being asked to divide $\frac{11}{8}$ cups into $\frac{3}{4}$-cup units.*

- How does the problem differ from the first example?

  - *The denominators are different.*

- What are some possible ways that we could divide these two fractions?

  - *I could rename $\frac{3}{4}$ as $\frac{6}{8}$. These fractions are equivalent. I created an equivalent fraction by multiplying $\frac{3}{4}$ by $\frac{2}{2}$.*

Lesson 4:   Interpreting and Computing Division of a Fraction by a Fraction—More   45
              Models

Example 2

Molly's friend, Xavier, also has $\frac{11}{8}$ cups of strawberries. He needs $\frac{3}{4}$ cup of strawberries to make a batch of tarts. How many batches can he make? Draw a model to support your solution.

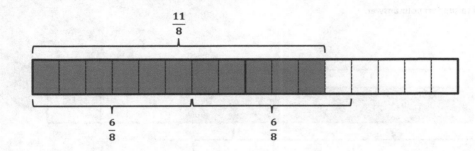

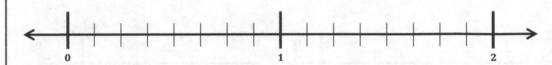

$$\frac{11}{8} \div \frac{6}{8} = 11 \text{ eighths} \div 6 \text{ eighths} = \frac{11}{6} = 1\frac{5}{6}$$

Xavier has enough to make 1 *and* $\frac{5}{6}$ *batches.*

MP.1

Example 3 (3 minutes)

- $\frac{6}{8} \div \frac{2}{8}$

- Yesterday we focused on measurement division. Let's solve this problem using partitive division. Therefore, what is the question asking?

  □ $\frac{6}{8}$ *is* $\frac{2}{8}$ *of what number?*

- How could we model this problem?

  □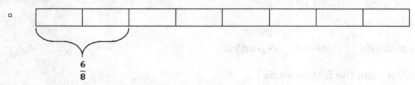

- Using the model, how could we solve the problem?

  □ 2 *units* = 6 *eighths*
  □ 1 *unit* = 6 *eighths* ÷ 2
  □ 1 *unit* = 3 *eighths*
  □ 8 *units* = 3 *eighths* × 8
  □ 8 *units* = 3

Lesson 4:   Interpreting and Computing Division of a Fraction by a Fraction—More
Models

EUREKA
MATH

MP.1

- Therefore, $\frac{6}{8} \div \frac{2}{8} = 3$.

- What do you notice about this solution that is similar to the solutions we found yesterday?

  □ *The units, eighths, cancel out.*

- This shows that we can follow the same process when solving both measurement and partitive division.

Example 3

Find the quotient: $\frac{6}{8} \div \frac{2}{8}$. Use a model to show your answer.

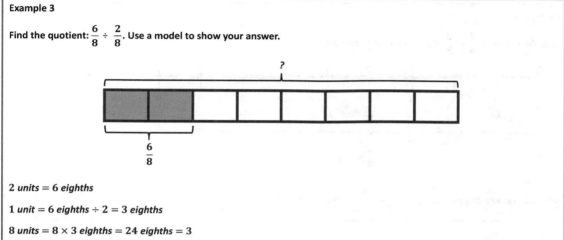

2 *units* = 6 *eighths*

1 *unit* = 6 *eighths* ÷ 2 = 3 *eighths*

8 *units* = 8 × 3 *eighths* = 24 *eighths* = 3

Example 4 (3 minutes)

- $\frac{3}{4} \div \frac{2}{3}$

- What is this question asking?

  □ *It could be either $\frac{2}{3}$ of what is $\frac{3}{4}$ or how many $\frac{2}{3}$ are in $\frac{3}{4}$?*

Lead students through a brief discussion about this example:

- Is your answer larger or smaller than one? Why?

  □ *Since $\frac{2}{3}$ is less than $\frac{3}{4}$, we will have an answer that is larger than 1.*

- What is the difference between this problem and the problems we completed in Lesson 3?

  □ *The fractions in this problem do not have common denominators, but the problems in Lesson 3 did.*

- Draw a model.

  □

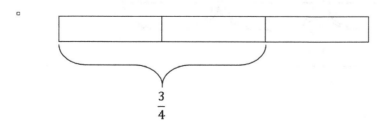

- How can we rewrite this question to make it easier to model?
  - □ *We can create equivalent fractions with like denominators and then model and divide.*
  - □ *We can also think of this as $\frac{9}{12} \div \frac{8}{12}$, or 9 twelfths divided by 8 twelfths. 9 units ÷ 8 units = $\frac{9}{8}$ or $1\frac{1}{8}$ units*

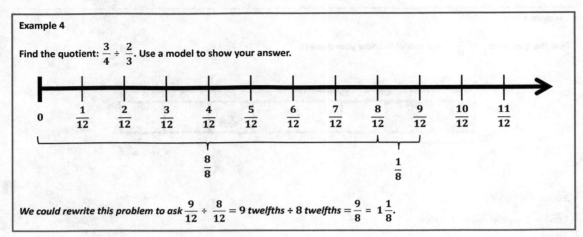

Example 4

Find the quotient: $\frac{3}{4} \div \frac{2}{3}$. Use a model to show your answer.

We could rewrite this problem to ask $\frac{9}{12} \div \frac{8}{12} = 9$ twelfths ÷ 8 twelfths = $\frac{9}{8} = 1\frac{1}{8}$.

Exercises 1–5 (19 minutes)

Students work in pairs or alone to solve more questions about division of fractions with unlike denominators.

Students are no longer required to draw models; however, models are provided in the answers in case some students still need the visual to complete the problems.

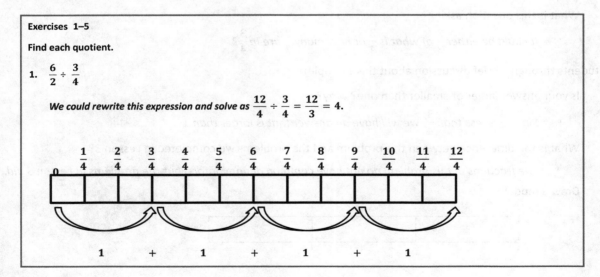

Exercises 1–5

Find each quotient.

1. $\frac{6}{2} \div \frac{3}{4}$

    We could rewrite this expression and solve as $\frac{12}{4} \div \frac{3}{4} = \frac{12}{3} = 4$.

EUREKA
MATH

2. $\dfrac{2}{3} \div \dfrac{2}{5}$

We could rewrite this expression and solve as $\dfrac{10}{15} \div \dfrac{6}{15} = \dfrac{10}{6} = 1\dfrac{4}{6}$.

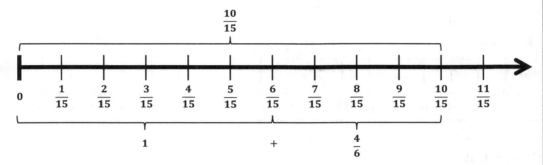

3. $\dfrac{7}{8} \div \dfrac{1}{2}$

We could rewrite this as $\dfrac{7}{8} \div \dfrac{4}{8} = \dfrac{7}{4} = 1\dfrac{3}{4}$.

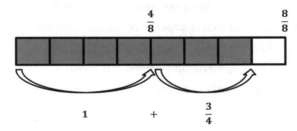

4. $\dfrac{3}{5} \div \dfrac{1}{4}$

This can be rewritten as $\dfrac{12}{20} \div \dfrac{5}{20} = \dfrac{12}{5} = 2\dfrac{2}{5}$.

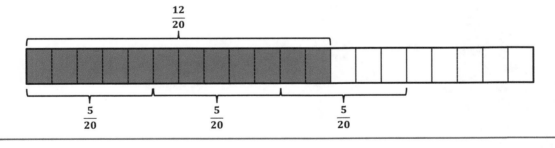

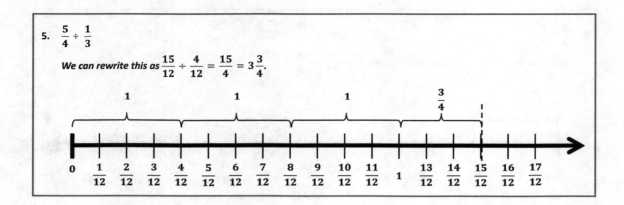

5. $\frac{5}{4} \div \frac{1}{3}$

We can rewrite this as $\frac{15}{12} \div \frac{4}{12} = \frac{15}{4} = 3\frac{3}{4}.$

Closing (10 minutes)

- When dividing fractions, is it possible to get a whole number quotient?
    - *It is possible to get a whole number quotient when dividing fractions.*
    - *When the dividend is larger than the divisor, the quotient will be greater than 1.*
- When dividing fractions, is it possible to get a quotient that is larger than the dividend?
    - *It is possible to get a quotient that is larger than the dividend when dividing fractions. For example,* $1 \div \frac{1}{4} = 4$ *fourths* $\div 1$ *fourth* $= 4.$
- When you are asked to divide two fractions with different denominators, what is one possible way to solve?
    - *To divide fractions with different denominators, we can find equivalent fractions with like denominators in order to solve.*

Exit Ticket (5 minutes)

Lesson 4:   Interpreting and Computing Division of a Fraction by a Fraction—More Models

EUREKA MATH

Name _____   Date_____

Lesson 4: Interpreting and Computing Division of a Fraction by a Fraction—More Models

Exit Ticket

Calculate each quotient. If needed, draw a model.

1. $\dfrac{9}{4} \div \dfrac{3}{8}$

2. $\dfrac{3}{5} \div \dfrac{2}{3}$

Exit Ticket Sample Solutions

Calculate each quotient. If needed, draw a model.

1. $\dfrac{9}{4} \div \dfrac{3}{8}$

   This can be rewritten as $\dfrac{18}{8} \div \dfrac{3}{8} =$ *18 eighths divided by 3 eighths* $= \dfrac{18}{3} = 6$.

   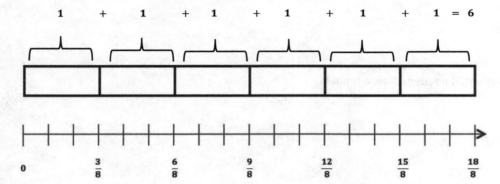

2. $\dfrac{3}{5} \div \dfrac{2}{3}$

   This can be rewritten as $\dfrac{9}{15} \div \dfrac{10}{15} =$ *9 fifteenths divided by 10 fifteenths, or 9 units ÷ 10 units.*

   So, this is equal to $\dfrac{9}{10}$.

   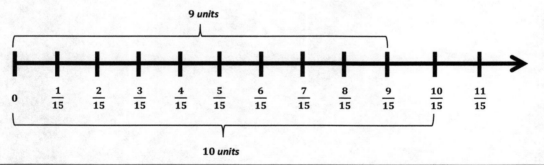

Lesson 4:   Interpreting and Computing Division of a Fraction by a Fraction—More
Models

EUREKA MATH

Problem Set Sample Solutions

The following problems can be used as extra practice or a homework assignment.

Calculate the quotient. If needed, draw a model.

1. $\dfrac{8}{9} \div \dfrac{4}{9}$

   8 *ninths* ÷ 4 *ninths* = 2

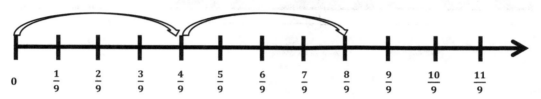

2. $\dfrac{9}{10} \div \dfrac{4}{10}$

   9 *tenths* ÷ 4 *tenths* = $2\dfrac{1}{4}$

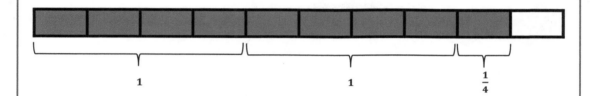

3. $\dfrac{3}{5} \div \dfrac{1}{3}$

   $\dfrac{9}{15} \div \dfrac{5}{15} = 9$ *fifteenths* ÷ 5 *fifteenths* $= \dfrac{9}{5} = 1\dfrac{4}{5}$

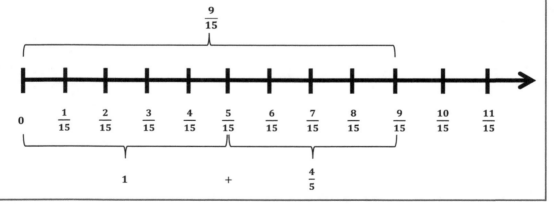

4. $\dfrac{3}{4} \div \dfrac{1}{5}$

$\dfrac{15}{20} \div \dfrac{4}{20} = 15 \text{ twentieths} \div 4 \text{ twentieths} = \dfrac{15}{4}$

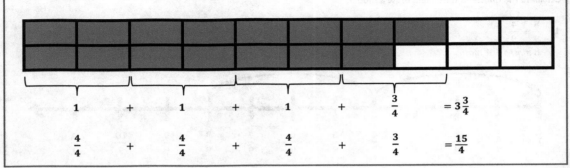

$$1 \quad + \quad 1 \quad + \quad 1 \quad + \quad \dfrac{3}{4} \quad = 3\dfrac{3}{4}$$

$$\dfrac{4}{4} \quad + \quad \dfrac{4}{4} \quad + \quad \dfrac{4}{4} \quad + \quad \dfrac{3}{4} \quad = \dfrac{15}{4}$$

Lesson 4:   Interpreting and Computing Division of a Fraction by a Fraction—More Models

EUREKA MATH

Lesson 5: Creating Division Stories

Student Outcomes

- Students demonstrate further understanding of division of fractions by creating their own word problems.
- Students select a measurement division problem, draw a model, find the answer, choose a unit, and set up a situation. They discover that they must try several situations and units before finding which ones are realistic with given numbers.

Lesson Notes

 During this lesson, students make sense of problems by creating them and persevering in solving them. They use concrete representations (fraction tiles or paper cutouts) and pictorial representations to show their understanding of the meaning of division and apply that understanding to the division of fractions.

There is a system for creating a division word problem. This sequence, which is noted in the second Student Outcome, is to be followed in order. Visual models showing examples of measurement division (e.g., $\frac{1}{2} \div \frac{1}{8}$ or how many $\frac{1}{8}$ are there in $\frac{1}{2}$?) should be available, visible, and referenced throughout the lesson. These can be from previous lessons, student work, chart paper, or board examples saved from Lessons 1–4 in this module. During the next lesson, partitive division problems ($50 \div \frac{2}{3}$ or 50 is $\frac{2}{3}$ of what number?) are the focus.

Before class, make a display of both types of problems (measurement and partitive).

It is helpful to put the "5 Steps for Creating Division Word Problems" on chart paper posted around the room.

Through previous lessons, students gained experience solving problems involving division with fractions and creating the corresponding models. Students now extend this work to choosing units and creating "division" stories. Pair up the students before the lesson so that they can collaborate on the exercises.

Classwork

Opening Exercise (5 minutes)

The classwork and problem sets from Lessons 1–4 include visual models made by the students which serve as the first three steps in writing division stories about the problems. The visual models include tape diagrams and number lines. Examples are as follows:

Opening Exercise

Tape Diagram:

$$\frac{8}{9} \div \frac{2}{9}$$

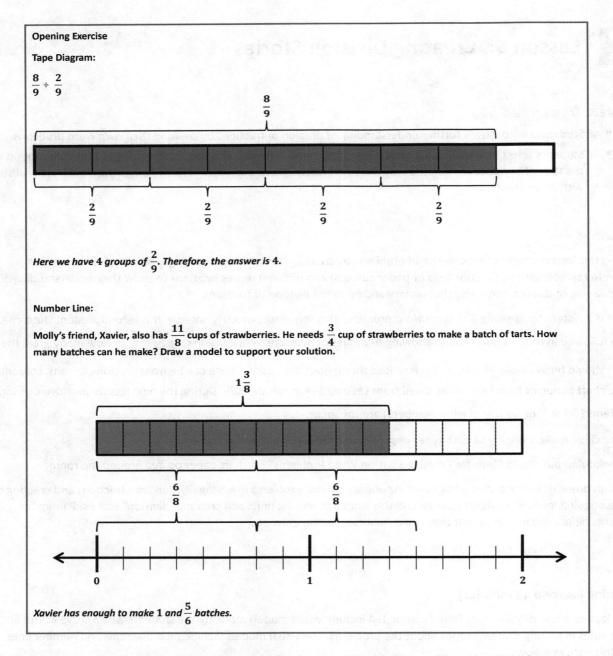

Here we have 4 groups of $\frac{2}{9}$. Therefore, the answer is 4.

Number Line:

Molly's friend, Xavier, also has $\frac{11}{8}$ cups of strawberries. He needs $\frac{3}{4}$ cup of strawberries to make a batch of tarts. How many batches can he make? Draw a model to support your solution.

Xavier has enough to make 1 and $\frac{5}{6}$ batches.

Use a few minutes to review the Problem Set from the last lesson. Ask students to add another model to each answer.

Discussion (5 minutes)

- In measurement division, the divisor names the size of the group (or unit), and the quotient represents the number of groups (or units). A measurement division problem can often be solved by thinking, "How many _____ are in _____?"

Lesson 5:   Creating Division Stories

EUREKA MATH

- Writing division stories involves five steps that are to be done in order. The steps are as follows: (1) decide on an interpretation (measurement or partitive); (2) draw a model; (3) find the answer; (4) choose a unit; and (5) set up a situation.

- Today, we work only on measurement division problems, and tomorrow, we will work on partitive division problems.

- By looking at all the work we have posted around the room, which of these steps are already done?

  □ *Steps 1, 2, and 3 are already done.*

- Today, we also focus on extending our work involving division with fractions to choosing units and setting up a story situation.

Example 1 (10 minutes)

In this example, students reason abstractly and quantitatively. They make sense of quantities and their relationships in problems and understand "how many" as it pertains to the divisor when finding the quotients of fractions.

> **Scaffolding:**
> Plastic fraction tile sets should be available for students who prefer a concrete model to handle. These are also useful for students who have difficulty making accurate sketches to show their work.

Encourage students to work each step in order.

- Let's look at an example of measurement division: $\frac{1}{2} \div \frac{1}{8}$ or how many $\frac{1}{8}$ are there in $\frac{1}{2}$?

- Our first step in writing a story problem is to decide which division interpretation to use.

Example 1

$$\frac{1}{2} \div \frac{1}{8}$$

Step 1: Decide on an interpretation.

For today, we will only use the measurement interpretation and consider the divisor, 1 eighth, to be the size of the group.

- Our second step is to sketch out a model. This should be done neatly and fairly accurately but should not take too long to do. Use a tape diagram or fraction bar to model this problem on your paper.

Step 2: Draw a model.

Note: This drawing can be cut and pasted onto an interactive whiteboard document and then labeled.

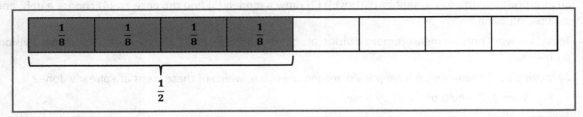

- The third step is to find the answer to the problem. Do this on your paper.

Step 3: Find the answer.

$$\frac{1}{2} \div \frac{1}{8} = \frac{4}{8} \div \frac{1}{8} = 4 \text{ eighths} \div 1 \text{ eighth} = 4$$

So, the answer is 4. There are four $\frac{1}{8}$ in $\frac{1}{2}$.

Step 4: Choose a unit.

Answers will vary, but pounds will be used throughout the discussion below.

Step 5: Set up a situation based upon the model.

Answers will vary, but there is a story problem provided in the discussion.

- Now that we have the answer, we can move on to the fourth step, choosing a unit. For measurement division, both divisor and dividend must be the same unit.

Note: Choosing the unit and using it in both the divisor and dividend consistently preserves the story situation clearly and precisely. With enough repetition, students learn to interpret and write division story problems more clearly.

- Let's use pounds for this example. We are asking how many $\frac{1}{8}$ pounds are in $\frac{1}{2}$ pound.

- Step 5 is to set up a situation. This means writing a story problem that includes all of the information necessary to solve it and that is also interesting, realistic, short, and clear. It may take several attempts before you find a story that works well with the given dividend and divisor.

- One story problem that might go well with these numbers is the following: Bonnie Baker has a total of $\frac{1}{2}$ pound of chocolate. She needs $\frac{1}{8}$ pound of chocolate for each batch of brownies she bakes. How many batches of brownies can Bonnie bake with $\frac{1}{2}$ pound of chocolate?

Exercise 1 (5 minutes)

Allow students to work with a partner to create the story problem. Also, take time to share and discuss their work.

EUREKA MATH

Exercise 1

Using the same dividend and divisor, work with a partner to create your own story problem. You may use the same unit, but your situation must be unique. You could try another unit such as ounces, yards, or miles if you prefer.

Possible story problems:

1. *Tina uses $\frac{1}{8}$ oz. of cinnamon each time she makes a batch of coffee cake topping. How many batches can she make if she has $\frac{1}{2}$ oz. left in her spice jar?*

2. *Eugenia has $\frac{1}{2}$ yard of ribbon. For each party decoration, she needs $\frac{1}{8}$ yard. How many party decorations can she make?*

Example 2 (7 minutes)

- Let's look at another example of measurement division: $\frac{3}{4} \div \frac{1}{2}$ or how many $\frac{1}{2}$ are there in $\frac{3}{4}$?

- Our first step in writing a story problem is to decide which division interpretation to use.

Example 2

$\frac{3}{4} \div \frac{1}{2}$

Step 1: Decide on an interpretation.

For today, we'll only use the measurement interpretation and consider the divisor, 1 half, to be the size of the group.

- Our second step is to sketch out a model. This should be done neatly and fairly accurately, but should not take too long to do. Use a tape diagram to model this problem on your paper.

Step 2: Draw a diagram.

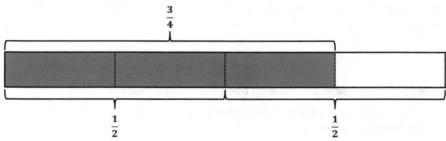

Step 3: Find the answer.

$\frac{3}{4} \div \frac{1}{2} = \frac{3}{4} \div \frac{2}{4} = 3 \text{ fourths} \div 2 \text{ fourths} = \frac{3}{2} = 1\frac{1}{2}$

So, the answer is $\frac{1}{2}$. There are $1\frac{1}{2}$ halves in $\frac{3}{4}$.

<table>
<tr><td>

Step 4: Choose a unit.

Answers will vary, but ounces will be used throughout the discussion below.

Step 5: Set up a situation based on the model.

Answers will vary, but there is a story problem provided in the discussion.

</td></tr>
</table>

- Step 4 is to choose a unit. Let's choose ounces.

- Step 5 is to set up a situation. This means writing a story problem that includes all of the information necessary to solve it and that is also interesting, realistic, short, and clear. It may take several attempts before you find a story that works well with the given dividend and divisor.

- One story problem that might go well with these numbers is the following: Tia has $\frac{3}{4}$ oz. of coffee grounds left in her coffee can. She needs $\frac{1}{2}$ oz. to make one cup of coffee. How many cups of coffee can she make?

Exercise 2 (5 minutes)

Allow students to work with a partner to create the story problem. Also, take time to share and discuss their work.

<table>
<tr><td>

Exercise 2

Using the same dividend and divisor, work with a partner to create your own story problem. You may use the same unit, but your situation must be unique. You could try another unit such as cups, yards, or miles if you prefer.

Possible story problems:

1. *Tiffany uses $\frac{1}{2}$ cup of glycerin each time she makes a batch of soap bubble mixture. How many batches can she make if she has $\frac{3}{4}$ cup left in her glycerin bottle?*

2. *Each jug holds $\frac{3}{4}$ gallon. Each bottle holds $\frac{1}{2}$ gallon. One jug has the same capcity as how many bottles?*

</td></tr>
</table>

Closing (5 minutes)

- How did we extend our work with division with fractions in this lesson?
  - *We took an answer to a measurement division problem, chose a unit, and then wrote a realistic story that fit the numbers and the unit.*

- What were your biggest challenges when writing story problems involving division with fractions?
  - *Accept all answers.*

Lesson 5:   Creating Division Stories

© 2015 Great Minds. eureka-math.org
G6-M2-TE-B2-1.3.1-01.2016

Lesson Summary

The method of creating division stories includes five steps:

Step 1: Decide on an interpretation (measurement or partitive). Today we used measurement division.

Step 2: Draw a model.

Step 3: Find the answer.

Step 4: Choose a unit.

Step 5: Set up a situation based on the model. This means writing a story problem that is interesting, realistic, and short. It may take several attempts before you find a story that works well with the given dividend and divisor.

Exit Ticket (3 minutes)

Name _____   Date _____

Lesson 5: Creating Division Stories

Exit Ticket

Write a story problem using the measurement interpretation of division for the following: $\frac{3}{4} \div \frac{1}{8} = 6$.

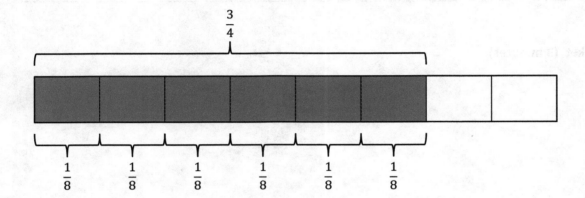

EUREKA
MATH

Exit Ticket Sample Solution

Write a story problem using the measurement interpretation of division for the following: $\frac{3}{4} \div \frac{1}{8} = 6$.

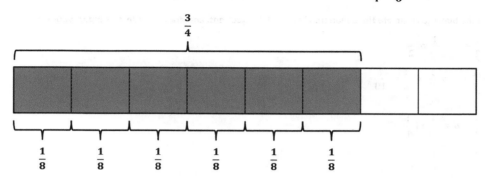

Arthur divided $\frac{3}{4}$ of his kingdom into parcels of land, each being $\frac{1}{8}$ of the entire kingdom. How many parcels did he make? *(Accept any other reasonable story problem showing $\frac{3}{4} \div \frac{1}{8} = 6$.)*

Problem Set Solutions

Solve.

1. How many sixteenths are in $\frac{15}{16}$?

    15 sixteenths ÷ 1 sixteenth = 15   *There are 15 sixteenths in $\frac{15}{16}$.*

2. How many $\frac{1}{4}$ teaspoon doses are in $\frac{7}{8}$ teaspoon of medicine?

    7 eighths ÷ 2 eighths = $\frac{7}{2}$ = $3\frac{1}{2}$ *There are $3\frac{1}{2}$ doses.*

3. How many $\frac{2}{3}$ cups servings are in a 4 cup container of food?

    12 thirds ÷ 2 thirds = 6   *There are 6 servings in the container.*

4. Write a measurement division story problem for $6 \div \frac{3}{4}$.

    Answers will vary.

5. Write a measurement division story problem for $\frac{5}{12} \div \frac{1}{6}$.

   Answers will vary.

6. Fill in the blank to complete the equation. Then, find the quotient, and draw a model to support your solution.

   a. $\frac{1}{2} \div 5 = \frac{1}{\square}$ of $\frac{1}{2}$

      $\frac{1}{2} \div 5 = \frac{1}{5}$ of $\frac{1}{2} = \frac{1}{10}$

   b. $\frac{3}{4} \div 6 = \frac{1}{\square}$ of $\frac{3}{4}$

      $\frac{3}{4} \div 6 = \frac{1}{6}$ of $\frac{3}{4} = \frac{3}{24}$

7. $\frac{4}{5}$ of the money collected from a fundrasier was divided equally among 8 grades. What fraction of the money did each grade receive?

   $\frac{4}{5} \div 8 = \frac{4}{5} \times \frac{1}{8} = \frac{4}{40} = \frac{1}{10}$ *Each grade got 1 tenth of the money.*

8. Meyer used 6 loads of gravel to cover $\frac{2}{5}$ of his driveway. How many loads of gravel will he need to cover his entire driveway?

   6 is $\frac{2}{5}$ group of what size?

   2 units = 6

   1 unit = 6 ÷ 2 = 3

   5 units = 5 × 3 = 15   *Meyer will need 15 loads.*

9. An athlete plans to run 3 miles. Each lap around the school yard is $\frac{3}{7}$ mile. How many laps will the athlete run?

   How many $\frac{3}{7}$ in 3?

   21 sevenths ÷ 3 sevenths = 7   *The athlete will run 7 laps.*

10. Parks spent $\frac{1}{3}$ of his money on a sweater. He spent $\frac{3}{5}$ of the remainder on a pair of jeans. If he has $36 left, how much did the sweater cost?

    $\frac{2}{5}$ *of* $\frac{2}{3} = \frac{6}{15}$ *$36 is $\frac{4}{15}$ of what number?*

    $\frac{1}{3} + \frac{6}{15} = \frac{11}{15}$ *4 units* = 36

    $\frac{4}{15}$ *of Parks's money is left over.*   *1 unit* = 36 ÷ 4 = 9

    5 units = 5 × 9 = 45

    The sweater cost $45.

Lesson 5:   Creating Division Stories

EUREKA
MATH

Lesson 6: More Division Stories

Student Outcomes

- Students demonstrate further understanding of division of fractions by creating their own word problems.
- Students choose a partitive division problem, draw a model, find the answer, choose a unit, and set up a situation. They also discover that they must try several situations and units before finding which ones are realistic with given numbers.

Lesson Notes

This lesson is a continuation of Lesson 5 and focuses on asking students to write fraction division story problems that are partitive in nature.

Classwork

Opening (5 minutes)

Provide students a few minutes to share the division stories they wrote for the previous lesson's problem set. Clarify any misconceptions that surface regarding the process of creating story problems when using measurement division.

Discussion (5 minutes)

- Partitive division is another interpretation of division problems. What do you recall about partitive division?

  - *In partitive division, the divisor tells the number of groups (or parts), and the quotient names the size of each group (or part).*

  - *When thinking of 24 ÷ 6 using the partitive division interpretation, I can think, "24 is 6 groups of what size? 24 is 6 groups of 4. The quotient 4, tells me the size of each group. There are 6 fours in 24."*

> **Scaffolding:**
>
> Paper fraction tile strips can be pre-cut for students who have difficulty making accurate sketches.

Example 1 (10 minutes)

- Today, we work with partitive division.

- Step 1: Let's find the quotient of $50 \div \frac{2}{3}$ using the partitive division interpretation.

Example 1

Divide $50 \div \dfrac{2}{3}$.

Step 1: Decide on an interpretation.

Today, we use the partitive interpretation and interpret the divisor, 2 thirds, to be the number of groups. I'm asking myself, "50 is 2 thirds group of what size?"

- Step 2: Draw a model. How many units do we draw? How do you know?
  - *The denominator of the fraction tells us we are using thirds. We need 3 units in in the tape diagram.*

> **Step 2: Draw a model.**

- The 50 represents how many of the units?
  - *50 is 2 thirds of the whole, so it represents 2 of the units of 1 third.*

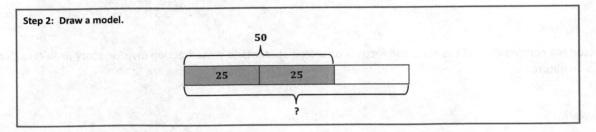

> **Step 2: Draw a model.**

- Step 3: Find the answer. In the partitive interpretation, $50 \div \frac{2}{3}$ means 50 is $\frac{2}{3}$ of some number. By looking at our tape diagram, we can see that 2 units are equal to 50, so we can divide by 2 to find that the value of 1 unit is 25. Then, in order to find the value of 3 units, we can multiply 3×25 to get 75.

Encourage students to recall the pattern they saw in Lesson 2. When dividing 50 by $\frac{2}{3}$, we can find the quotient by dividing by 2 and then multiplying by 3.

> **Step 3: Find the answer.**
>
> 2 *units* = 50
>
> 1 *unit* = 50 ÷ 2 = 25
>
> 3 *units* = 3 × 25 = 75
>
> **Step 4: Choose a unit.**
>
> *Answers will vary, but dollars will be used throughout the discussion below.*
>
> **Step 5: Set up a situation based upon the model.**
>
> *Answers will vary, but there is a story problem provided in the discussion.*

- Now that we have the answer, we can move on to the fourth step, choosing a unit. Money units are often convenient for making word problems. Using dollars as the unit, we are looking for a situation where $\frac{2}{3}$ of some dollar amount is $50.

EUREKA MATH

- Step 5 is to set up a situation based upon the model. Remember that this means writing a story problem that includes all of the information necessary to solve it and that is also interesting, realistic, short, and clear. It may take several attempts before you find a story that works well with the given dividend and divisor.

- Spending money gives a "before and after" word problem. We are looking for a situation where $\frac{2}{3}$ of some greater dollar amount is $50.

- One story problem that might go well with these numbers is the following: Adam spent $50 on a new graphing calculator. This was $\frac{2}{3}$ of his money. How much money did he start with?

Exercise 1 (5 minutes)

Allow students to work with a partner to create the story problem. Also, take time to share and discuss their work.

Exercise 1

Using the same dividend and divisor, work with a partner to create your own story problem. You may use the same unit, dollars, but your situation must be unique. You could try another unit, such as miles, if you prefer.

Possible story problems:

1. *Ronaldo has ridden 50 miles during his bicycle race and is $\frac{2}{3}$ of the way to the finish line. How long is the race?*

2. *Samantha used 50 tickets ($\frac{2}{3}$ of her total) to trade for a kewpie doll at the fair. How many tickets did she start with?*

Example 2 (10 minutes)

- Step 1: Let's find the quotient of $\frac{1}{2} \div \frac{3}{4}$ using the partitive division interpretation.

Example 2

Divide $\frac{1}{2} \div \frac{3}{4}$.

Step 1: Decide on an interpretation.

Today, we use the partitive interpretation and interpret the divisor, 3 fourths, to be the number of groups. I'm asking myself, "1 half is 3 fourths of what number?"

- Step 2: Draw a model. How many units do we draw? How do you know?
  - *The denominator of the fraction tells us we are using fourths. We need 4 units in in the tape diagram.*

Step 2: Draw a model.

- 1 half represents how many of the units?
  - $\frac{1}{2}$ is 3 fourths, so it represents 3 of the units of 1 fourth.

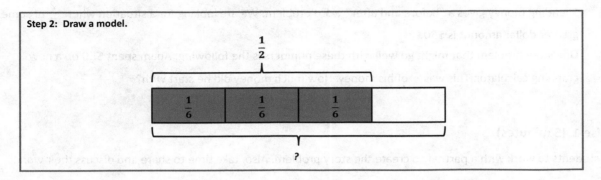

Step 2: Draw a model.

- Step 3: Find the answer. In the partitive interpretation, $\frac{1}{2} \div \frac{3}{4}$ means 1 half is $\frac{3}{4}$ of some number. By looking at our tape diagram, we can see that 3 units are equal to $\frac{1}{2}$, so we can divide by 3 to find that the value of 1 unit is $\frac{1}{6}$. Then, in order to find the value of 4 units, we can multiply $4 \times (1 \text{ sixth})$ to get 4 sixths.

Step 3: Find the answer.

3 *units* $= \dfrac{1}{2}$

1 *unit* $= \dfrac{1}{2} \div 3 = \dfrac{1}{3}$ *of* $\dfrac{1}{2} = \dfrac{1}{6}$

4 *units* $= 4 \times 1$ *sixth* $= 4$ *sixths* $= \dfrac{4}{6}$

Step 4: Choose a unit.

Answers will vary.

Step 5: Set up a situation based upon the model.

Answers will vary.

- Now that we have the answer, we can move on to the fourth step, choosing a unit. In this example, both the dividend and the quotient are a fraction. Therefore, the unit we choose has to be such that $\frac{1}{2}$ and $\frac{4}{6}$ both make sense. Time (in hours), distance (in feet), and eggs (in dozens) are good options since both halves and sixths are identifiable parts of an hour, a foot, and a dozen.

- Step 5: Set up a situation based upon the model. Remember that this means writing a story problem that includes all of the information necessary to solve it and that is interesting, realistic, short, and clear. It may take several attempts before you find a story that works well with the given dividend and divisor.

- One story problem that might go well with these numbers is the following: After traveling for a half hour, Scott completed $\frac{3}{4}$ of his commute. How long is commute?

Exercise 2 (5 minutes)

Allow students to work with a partner to create the story problem. Also, take time to share and discuss their work.

Exercise 2

Using the same dividend and divisor, work with a partner to create your own story problem. Try a different unit.

Possible story problems:

1. *Daryl completed 3 fourths of his homework in a half hour. How long does it take Daryl to complete all of his homework?*

2. *A snail saw food sitting a distance away. After traveling for a half foot, a snail had covered $\frac{3}{4}$ the distance. How far away was the food?*

Closing (3 minutes)

- How did we extend our work with division with fractions in this lesson?
  - *We took an answer to a partitive division problem, chose a unit, and then thought of a story problem that would fit it.*
- What were your biggest challenges when writing story problems involving division with fractions?
  - *Accept all answers.*

Exit Ticket (2 minutes)

Name _____ Date _____

Lesson 6: More Division Stories

Exit Ticket

Write a story problem using the partitive interpretation of division for the following: $25 \div \dfrac{5}{8} = 40$.

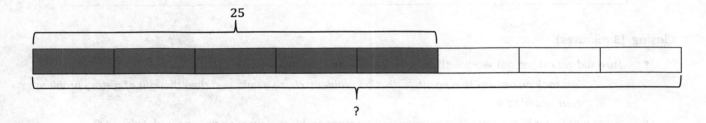

Exit Ticket Sample Solutions

Write a story problem using the partitive interpretation of division for the following: $25 \div \frac{5}{8} = 40$.

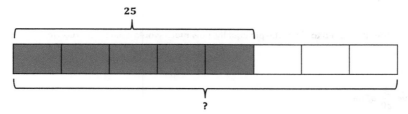

Zolanda spent $\frac{5}{8}$ of her class period, or 25 minutes, taking notes. How long was the class period? (Accept any other reasonable story problem showing $25 \div \frac{5}{8} = 40$.)

Problem Set Sample Solutions

Solve.

1. $\frac{15}{16}$ is 1 sixteenth groups of what size?

    15 *sixteenths* ÷ 1 *sixteenth* = 15. *The size of the group is* 15.

2. $\frac{7}{8}$ teaspoons is $\frac{1}{4}$ groups of what size?

    7 *eighths* ÷ 2 *eighths* $= \frac{7}{2} = 3\frac{1}{2}$. *The size of the group is* $3\frac{1}{2}$.

3. A 4-cup container of food is $\frac{2}{3}$ groups of what size?

    12 *thirds* ÷ 2 *thirds* = 6. *The size of the group is* 6.

4. Write a partitive division story problem for $6 \div \frac{3}{4}$.

    Answers will vary.

5. Write a partitive division story problem for $\frac{5}{12} \div \frac{1}{6}$.

    Answers will vary.

6. Fill in the blank to complete the equation. Then, find the quotient, and draw a model to support your solution.

    a. $\frac{1}{4} \div 7 = \frac{1}{\square}$ of $\frac{1}{4}$

    $\frac{1}{4} \div 7 = \frac{1}{7}$ of $\frac{1}{4} = \frac{1}{28}$

b. $\dfrac{5}{6} \div 4 = \dfrac{1}{\square}$ of $\dfrac{5}{6}$

   $\dfrac{5}{6} \div 4 = \dfrac{1}{4}$ of $\dfrac{5}{6} = \dfrac{5}{24}$

7. There is $\dfrac{3}{5}$ of a pie left. If 4 friends wanted to share the pie equally, how much would each friend receive?

   $\dfrac{3}{5} \div 4 = \dfrac{3}{5} \times \dfrac{1}{4} = \dfrac{3}{20}$

   Each friend would receive $\dfrac{3}{20}$ of the pie.

8. In two hours, Holden completed $\dfrac{3}{4}$ of his race. How long will it take Holden to complete the entire race?

   $2 \div \dfrac{3}{4} = 8 \ fourths \div 3 \ fourths = \dfrac{8}{3} = 2\dfrac{2}{3}$

   It will take Holden $2\dfrac{2}{3}$ hours to complete the race.

9. Sam cleaned $\dfrac{1}{3}$ of his house in 50 minutes. How many hours will it take him to clean his entire house?

   $50 \ minutes = \dfrac{1}{60} \dfrac{hour}{minutes} = \dfrac{5}{6} \ hours$

   $\dfrac{5}{6} \div \dfrac{1}{3} = 5 \ sixths \div 2 \ sixths = \dfrac{5}{2} = 2\dfrac{1}{2}$

   It will take Sam $2\dfrac{1}{2}$ hours to clean his entire house.

10. It took Mario 10 months to beat $\dfrac{5}{8}$ of the levels on his new video game. How many years will it take for Mario to beat all the levels?

   $10 \ months = \dfrac{1}{12} \dfrac{years}{months} = \dfrac{10}{12} \ years = \dfrac{5}{6} \ years$

   $\dfrac{5}{6} \div \dfrac{5}{8} = \dfrac{20}{24} \div \dfrac{15}{24} = \dfrac{20}{15} = 1\dfrac{1}{3}$

   Mario will need $1\dfrac{1}{3}$ years to beat all the levels.

11. A recipe calls for $1\dfrac{1}{2}$ cups of sugar. Marley only has measuring cups that measure $\dfrac{1}{4}$ cup. How many times will Marley have to fill the measuring cup?

   $1\dfrac{1}{4} \div \dfrac{1}{4} = \dfrac{3}{2} \div \dfrac{1}{4} = \dfrac{6}{4} \div \dfrac{1}{4} = 6$

   Marley will have to use the measuring cup 6 times.

EUREKA MATH

Lesson 7: The Relationship Between Visual Fraction Models and Equations

Student Outcomes

- Students formally connect models of fraction division to multiplication and the invert-and-multiply rule, in particular.

Lesson Notes

In each example that students work through, the concept is reinforced: dividing by a fraction yields the same result as multiplying by the inverse of that fraction. Students see that this holds true whether the context is partitive or measurement in nature.

The terms *multiplicative inverse* and *reciprocal* should be defined and displayed in the classroom, perhaps as part of a Word Wall.

Two numbers whose product is one are multiplicative inverses. We can always find the multiplicative inverse by taking the reciprocal, as shown.

$$\frac{2}{3} \implies \frac{3}{2}$$

$$\frac{5}{8} \implies \frac{8}{5}$$

$$4 \implies \frac{1}{4}$$

Pre-cut fraction strips are provided at the end of this document as a scaffold for students who struggle to draw models.

Classwork

Opening (4 minutes)

Introduce the definition of the term *multiplicative inverse:* Two numbers whose product is 1 are multiplicative inverses of one another. For example, $\frac{3}{4}$ and $\frac{4}{3}$ are multiplicative inverses of one another because $\frac{3}{4} \times \frac{4}{3} = \frac{4}{3} \times \frac{3}{4} = 1$.

Point out and ask students to write several of their own examples of multiplicative inverses. The general form of the concept $\frac{a}{b} \times \frac{b}{a} = \frac{b}{a} \times \frac{a}{b} = 1$ should also be displayed in several places throughout the classroom.

MP.1 During this lesson, students continue to make sense of problems and persevere in solving them. They use concrete representations when understanding the meaning of division and apply it to the division of fractions. They ask themselves, "What is this problem asking me to find?" For instance, when determining the quotient of fractions, students may ask themselves how many sets or groups of the divisor are in the dividend. That quantity is the quotient of the problem.

EUREKA MATH   **Lesson 7:**   The Relationship Between Visual Fraction Models and Equations   **73**

Example 1 (15 minutes)

Consider the following, an example that we have worked with in previous lessons:

Example 1

Model the following using a partitive interpretation.

$$\frac{3}{4} \div \frac{2}{5}$$

$\frac{2}{5}$ *of what number is* $\frac{3}{4}$*?*

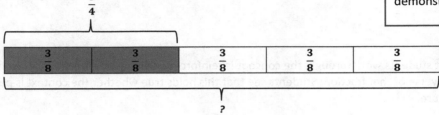

Shade 2 of the 5 sections $\left(\frac{2}{5}\right)$.

Label the part that is known $\left(\frac{3}{4}\right)$.

Make notes below on the math sentences needed to solve the problem.

Let's relate what we just did to multiplication.

- Look back at the model. What was the first thing you did? What was the next thing you did?

  - *We found half of* $\frac{3}{4}$. *Then we took the result and multiplied by 5.*

- We can record this process using multiplication:

$$\frac{3}{4} \div \frac{2}{5} = \left(\frac{1}{2} \cdot \frac{3}{4}\right) \cdot 5$$

- How can you show that $\left(\frac{1}{2} \cdot \frac{3}{4}\right) \cdot 5$ is equivalent to $\frac{3}{4} \cdot \frac{5}{2}$? What does that tell you about $\frac{3}{4} \div \frac{2}{5}$ and $\frac{3}{4} \times \frac{5}{2}$?

  - *Since we are multiplying, we can rearrange the order of our factors:*

$$\frac{1}{2} \cdot \frac{3}{4} \cdot 5 = \frac{3}{4} \cdot \left(\frac{1}{2} \cdot 5\right) = \frac{3}{4} \cdot \frac{5}{2}.$$

  Since $\frac{3}{4} \div \frac{2}{5}$ *is equal to* $\left(\frac{1}{2} \cdot \frac{3}{4}\right) \cdot 5$, *and that's equal to* $\frac{3}{4} \cdot \frac{5}{2}$, *we can say that* $\frac{3}{4} \div \frac{2}{5} = \frac{3}{4} \cdot \frac{5}{2}$.

- To solve this division problem, we can invert the divisor and multiply. This is called the *invert and multiply* method.

EUREKA MATH

Example 2 (10 minutes)

Consider the following, an example that we have worked with in previous lessons:

Example 2

Model the following using a measurement interpretation.

$\dfrac{3}{5} \div \dfrac{1}{4}$

$\dfrac{3}{5}$ *is how many fourths?*

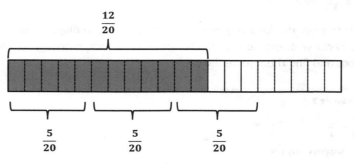

Convert the whole and the divisor to the same fractional units first. Then divide the numerators.

$\dfrac{3}{5} \div \dfrac{1}{4} = \dfrac{12}{20} \div \dfrac{5}{20} = 12$ *twentieths* $\div\ 5$ *twentieths* $= \dfrac{12}{5} = 2\dfrac{2}{5}$

In what follows, we discuss the fact that the invert and multiply rule produces the same result as finding like denominators and dividing the numerators.

- Does this produce the same result as inverting the divisor and multiplying? In other words, is $\dfrac{3}{5} \div \dfrac{1}{4}$ equal to $\dfrac{3}{5} \times \dfrac{4}{1}$?

  □ *Yes, in both cases we get $\dfrac{12}{5}$ or $2\dfrac{2}{5}$.*

- To see why this always works, let's take a closer look at how we solved this problem.

- First, we found like denominators:

$$\dfrac{3}{5} \div \dfrac{1}{4} = \dfrac{3 \cdot 4}{5 \cdot 4} \div \dfrac{1 \cdot 5}{4 \cdot 5}$$

- Instead of multiplying out the numerators and denominators like we did before, let's leave them in factored form for now. Since the denominators are the same, what should we do next?

  □ *Divide the numerators.*

- So we get:

$$\dfrac{3}{5} \div \dfrac{1}{4} = \dfrac{3 \cdot 4}{5 \cdot 4} \div \dfrac{1 \cdot 5}{4 \cdot 5} = \dfrac{3 \cdot 4}{1 \cdot 5}$$

- Is the final expression, at right, equal to $\dfrac{3}{5} \cdot \dfrac{4}{1}$? How can you show that?

  □ *Yes. You can multiply in any order so, $\dfrac{3 \cdot 4}{1 \cdot 5} = \dfrac{3 \cdot 4}{5 \cdot 1}$. And that's just what you get when you multiply $\dfrac{3}{5} \cdot \dfrac{4}{1}$.*

MP.8

MP.8

- Does this process always work? Can you always divide by inverting the divisor and multiplying?
    □ *I think so. When you find like denominators, you multiply the numerator and denominator in the whole and the divisor by the other denominator. Then when you divide the numerators, it will just be the same thing you get when you invert and multiply.*

Example 3 (8 minutes)

Ask students to solve the following problem with both a tape diagram and the *invert and multiply* rule. Allow them to use either a partitive or measurement interpretation in their model. They should compare the answers obtained from both methods and find them to be the same.

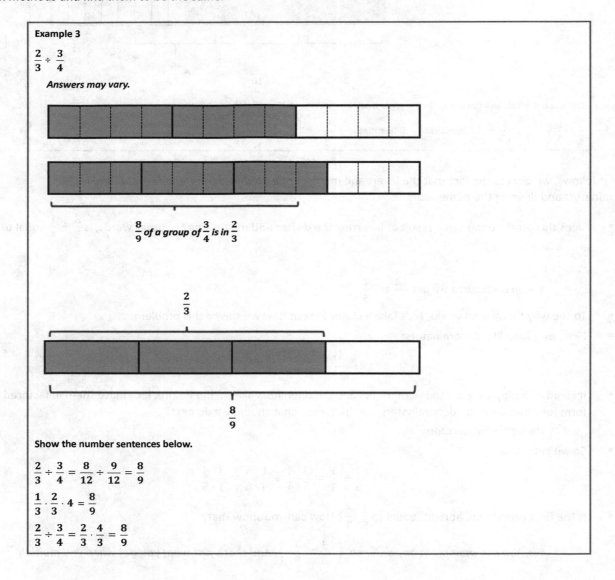

Example 3

$\dfrac{2}{3} \div \dfrac{3}{4}$

Answers may vary.

$\dfrac{8}{9}$ *of a group of* $\dfrac{3}{4}$ *is in* $\dfrac{2}{3}$

$\dfrac{2}{3}$

$\dfrac{8}{9}$

Show the number sentences below.

$$\frac{2}{3} \div \frac{3}{4} = \frac{8}{12} \div \frac{9}{12} = \frac{8}{9}$$

$$\frac{1}{3} \cdot \frac{2}{3} \cdot 4 = \frac{8}{9}$$

$$\frac{2}{3} \div \frac{3}{4} = \frac{2}{3} \cdot \frac{4}{3} = \frac{8}{9}$$

Lesson 7:   The Relationship Between Visual Fraction Models and Equations

EUREKA MATH

Invite two students, one who used a partitive interpretation and one who used a measurement interpretation, to present their solutions.

- Do the models used by each student look the same or different?
  - *Different. One shows $\frac{3}{4}$ of some whole, but the other shows groups of $\frac{3}{4}$.*

- Did they arrive at the same result?
  - *Yes, both of them got $\frac{8}{9}$.*

- What about their work when they used the invert and multiply rule? Is there any difference between their work in that case?
  - *No, to use the invert and multiply rule, you just invert the divisor and multiply. It doesn't matter whether it's partitive or measurement division.*

Closing (3 minutes)

- Dividing by a fraction is equivalent to multiplying by its reciprocal, or multiplicative inverse. We call this the *invert and multiply* rule.

- Does it matter which interpretation of division we use? Can we always invert and multiply?
  - *No, it does not matter. The invert and multiply rule works for any division problem.*

Lesson Summary

Connecting models of fraction division to multiplication through the use of reciprocals helps in understanding the *invert and multiply* rule. That is, given two fractions $\frac{a}{b}$ and $\frac{c}{d}$, we have the following:

$$\frac{a}{b} \div \frac{c}{d} = \frac{a}{b} \times \frac{d}{c}.$$

Exit Ticket (5 minutes)

Name _____ Date _____

Lesson 7: The Relationship Between Visual Fraction Models and Equations

Exit Ticket

1. Write the reciprocal of the following numbers.

Number	$\frac{7}{10}$	$\frac{1}{2}$	5
Reciprocal			

2. Rewrite this division expression as an equivalent multiplication expression: $\frac{5}{8} \div \frac{2}{3}$.

3. Solve Problem 2. Draw a model to support your solution.

EUREKA
MATH

Exit Ticket Sample Solutions

1. Write the reciprocal of the following numbers.

Number	$\frac{7}{10}$	$\frac{1}{2}$	5
Reciprocal	$\frac{10}{7}$	2	$\frac{1}{5}$

2. Rewrite this division expression as an equivalent multiplication expression: $\frac{5}{8} \div \frac{2}{3}$.

$$\frac{5}{8} \cdot \frac{2}{3} \ or \ \frac{1}{2} \cdot \frac{5}{8} \cdot 3$$

3. Solve Problem 2. Draw a model to support your solution.

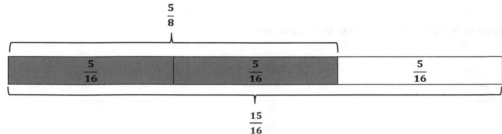

Answer:

$$\frac{5}{8} \div \frac{2}{3} = \frac{5}{8} \cdot \frac{3}{2} = \frac{15}{16}$$

Problem Set Sample Solutions

Invert and multiply to divide.

1.

a. $\frac{2}{3} \div \frac{1}{4} = \frac{2}{3} \times \frac{4}{1} = \frac{8}{3}$

b. $\frac{2}{3} \div 4 = \frac{2}{3} \times \frac{1}{4} = \frac{1}{6}$

c. $4 \div \frac{2}{3} = 4 \times \frac{3}{2} = 6$

2.

a. $\frac{1}{3} \div \frac{1}{4} = \frac{1}{3} \times \frac{4}{1} = \frac{4}{3}$

b. $\frac{1}{8} \div \frac{3}{4} = \frac{1}{8} \times \frac{4}{3} = \frac{1}{6}$

c. $\frac{9}{4} \div \frac{6}{5} = \frac{9}{4} \times \frac{5}{6} = \frac{15}{8}$

3.

a. $\frac{2}{3} \div \frac{3}{4} = \frac{2}{3} \times \frac{4}{3} = \frac{8}{9}$

b. $\frac{3}{5} \div \frac{3}{2} = \frac{3}{5} \times \frac{2}{3} = \frac{2}{5}$

c. $\frac{22}{4} \div \frac{2}{5} = \frac{22}{4} \times \frac{5}{2} = \frac{55}{4}$

4. Summer used $\frac{2}{5}$ of her ground beef to make burgers. If she used $\frac{3}{4}$ pounds of beef, how much beef did she have at first?

    $\frac{3}{4}$ *is* $\frac{2}{5}$ *of what? So,* $\frac{3}{4} \div \frac{2}{5} = \frac{3}{4} \times \frac{5}{2} = \frac{15}{8} = 1\frac{7}{8}$.

5. Alistair has 5 half-pound chocolate bars. It takes $1\frac{1}{2}$ pounds of chocolate, broken into chunks, to make a batch of cookies. How many batches can Alistair make with the chocolate he has on hand?

    $1\frac{1}{2} = \frac{3}{2}$

    $\frac{5}{2}$ *is how many* $\frac{3}{2}$?

    $\frac{5}{2} \div \frac{3}{2} = \frac{5}{2} \times \frac{2}{3} = \frac{5}{3}$

    Alistair can only make 1 full batch, but he has enough to make another $\frac{2}{3}$ *batch.*

6. Draw a model that shows $\frac{2}{5} \div \frac{1}{3}$. Find the answer as well.

    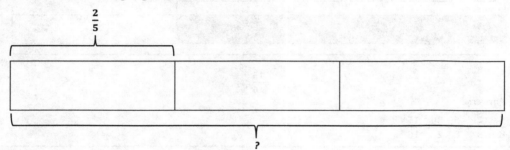

    Answer:

    $\frac{2}{5} \div \frac{1}{3} = \frac{2}{5} \cdot \frac{3}{1} = \frac{6}{5}$ *or* $1\frac{1}{5}$

7. Draw a model that shows $\frac{3}{4} \div \frac{1}{2}$. Find the answer as well.

    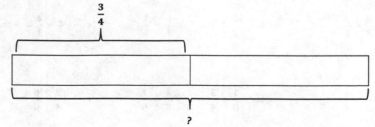

    Answer:

    $\frac{3}{4} \div \frac{1}{2} = \frac{3}{4} \cdot \frac{2}{1} = \frac{6}{4}$ *or* $1\frac{1}{2}$

Lesson 7:   The Relationship Between Visual Fraction Models and Equations

EUREKA MATH

1 whole unit											

$\frac{1}{2}$ $\frac{1}{2}$

$\frac{1}{3}$ $\frac{1}{3}$ $\frac{1}{3}$

$\frac{1}{4}$ $\frac{1}{4}$ $\frac{1}{4}$ $\frac{1}{4}$

$\frac{1}{5}$ $\frac{1}{5}$ $\frac{1}{5}$ $\frac{1}{5}$ $\frac{1}{5}$

$\frac{1}{6}$ $\frac{1}{6}$ $\frac{1}{6}$ $\frac{1}{6}$ $\frac{1}{6}$ $\frac{1}{6}$

$\frac{1}{8}$ $\frac{1}{8}$ $\frac{1}{8}$ $\frac{1}{8}$ $\frac{1}{8}$ $\frac{1}{8}$ $\frac{1}{8}$ $\frac{1}{8}$

$\frac{1}{9}$ $\frac{1}{9}$ $\frac{1}{9}$ $\frac{1}{9}$ $\frac{1}{9}$ $\frac{1}{9}$ $\frac{1}{9}$ $\frac{1}{9}$ $\frac{1}{9}$

$\frac{1}{10}$ $\frac{1}{10}$ $\frac{1}{10}$ $\frac{1}{10}$ $\frac{1}{10}$ $\frac{1}{10}$ $\frac{1}{10}$ $\frac{1}{10}$ $\frac{1}{10}$ $\frac{1}{10}$

$\frac{1}{12}$ $\frac{1}{12}$ $\frac{1}{12}$ $\frac{1}{12}$ $\frac{1}{12}$ $\frac{1}{12}$ $\frac{1}{12}$ $\frac{1}{12}$ $\frac{1}{12}$ $\frac{1}{12}$ $\frac{1}{12}$ $\frac{1}{12}$

Lesson 8: Dividing Fractions and Mixed Numbers

Student Outcomes

- Students divide fractions by mixed numbers by first converting the mixed numbers into a fraction with a value larger than one.
- Students use equations to find quotients.

Lesson Notes

There is some mandatory prep work before teaching this lesson. The memory game that is included in this lesson needs to be cut and prepared for pairs or individual students.

Classwork

Example 1 (12 minutes): Introduction to Calculating the Quotient of a Mixed Number and a Fraction

- Carli has $4\frac{1}{2}$ walls left to paint in order for all the bedrooms in her house to have the same color paint. However, she has used almost all of her paint and only has $\frac{5}{6}$ of a gallon left. How much paint can she use on each wall in order to have enough to paint the remaining walls?

- In order to solve the word problem, we must calculate the quotient of $\frac{5}{6} \div 4\frac{1}{2}$.

Before dividing, discuss how the answer must be less than one because you are dividing a smaller number by a larger number. Estimation could also be used to emphasize this point: $1 \div 5 = \frac{1}{5}$.

Explain that the mixed number must be converted into a fraction with a value larger than one. You may also emphasize that converting mixed numbers to fractions with a value larger than one is important for different division strategies. Have students complete this conversion on their own and share the process they followed.

Remind students about the formula they learned in the previous lesson; then, have them attempt to solve the problem. Have students show the process they used to find the quotient.

> **Scaffolding:**
>
> If students struggle with converting mixed numbers into fractions, a model may help. On a number line, show students how 9 steps of length $\frac{1}{2}$ ends up at $4\frac{1}{2}$.
>
>

EUREKA
MATH

Example 1: Introduction to Calculating the Quotient of a Mixed Number and a Fraction

a.   Carli has $4\frac{1}{2}$ walls left to paint in order for all the bedrooms in her house to have the same color paint.

However, she has used almost all of her paint and only has $\frac{5}{6}$ of a gallon left.

How much paint can she use on each wall in order to have enough to paint the remaining walls?

Write the expression: $\frac{5}{6} \div 4\frac{1}{2}$

Convert into a fraction: $\frac{9}{2}$

Divide fraction: $\frac{5}{6} \div \frac{9}{2} = \frac{5}{6} \times \frac{2}{9} = \frac{10}{54}$ or $\frac{5}{27}$

Carli can use $\frac{5}{27}$ *of a gallon of paint on each of the remaining walls.*

- Calculate the quotient. $\frac{2}{5} \div 3\frac{4}{7}$

Students solve this problem individually as the teacher walks around checking for understanding. Students then share their answers and processes used to find the quotients. Provide time for students to ask questions.

b.   **Calculate the quotient.**

$\frac{2}{5} \div 3\frac{4}{7}$

Convert into a fraction: $\frac{25}{7}$

Divide fractions: $\frac{2}{5} \div \frac{25}{7} = \frac{2}{5} \times \frac{7}{25} = \frac{14}{125}$

Exercise (25 minutes)

Students complete the memory game individually or in small groups.

The following are some important directions for the teacher to share with students:

MP.1

- The goal is to match each expression with the equivalent quotient. For the cards to match, it may be necessary to rewrite the quotient as a mixed number or equivalent fraction.

- Each expression is assigned a letter. Students must show their work in that box on the student materials. Once they have solved a particular problem, they do not have to solve it again if they record their work in the correct place.

- Students are able to flip two cards over during each turn. If the expression and the quotient do not match, both cards should be flipped back over. If the expression and quotient do match, the student keeps the matches to determine a winner at the end.

If students are not clear about the directions, the teacher may choose two or three problems for students to do as a class to show how the memory game works.

Exercise

Show your work for the memory game in the boxes provided below.

A.	$\frac{3}{4} \div 6\frac{2}{3} = \frac{3}{4} \div \frac{20}{3} = \frac{3}{4} \times \frac{3}{20} = \frac{9}{80}$
B.	$\frac{1}{3} \div 4\frac{3}{4} = \frac{1}{3} \div \frac{19}{4} = \frac{1}{3} \times \frac{4}{19} = \frac{4}{57}$
C.	$\frac{2}{5} \div 1\frac{7}{8} = \frac{2}{5} \div \frac{15}{8} = \frac{2}{5} \times \frac{8}{15} = \frac{16}{75}$
D.	$7\frac{1}{2} \div \frac{5}{6} = \frac{15}{2} \div \frac{5}{6} = \frac{15}{2} \times \frac{6}{5} = \frac{90}{10} = 9$
E.	$3\frac{4}{7} \div \frac{5}{8} = \frac{25}{7} \div \frac{5}{8} = \frac{25}{7} \times \frac{8}{5} = \frac{200}{35} = 5\frac{5}{7}$
F.	$5\frac{5}{8} \div \frac{9}{10} = \frac{45}{8} \div \frac{9}{10} = \frac{45}{8} \times \frac{10}{9} = \frac{450}{72} = 6\frac{1}{4}$
G.	$\frac{1}{4} \div 10\frac{11}{12} = \frac{1}{4} \div \frac{131}{12} = \frac{1}{4} \times \frac{12}{131} = \frac{12}{524} = \frac{3}{131}$
H.	$5\frac{3}{4} \div \frac{5}{9} = \frac{23}{4} \div \frac{5}{9} = \frac{23}{4} \times \frac{9}{5} = \frac{207}{20} = 10\frac{7}{20}$
I.	$3\frac{1}{5} \div \frac{2}{3} = \frac{16}{5} \div \frac{2}{3} = \frac{16}{5} \times \frac{3}{2} = \frac{48}{10} = 4\frac{4}{5}$
J.	$\frac{3}{5} \div 3\frac{1}{7} = \frac{3}{5} \div \frac{22}{7} = \frac{3}{5} \times \frac{7}{22} = \frac{21}{110}$
K.	$\frac{10}{13} \div 2\frac{4}{7} = \frac{10}{13} \div \frac{18}{7} = \frac{10}{13} \times \frac{7}{18} = \frac{70}{234} = \frac{35}{117}$
L.	$2\frac{1}{4} \div \frac{7}{8} = \frac{9}{4} \div \frac{7}{8} = \frac{9}{4} \times \frac{8}{7} = \frac{72}{28} = 2\frac{4}{7}$

Closing (4 minutes)

- How does the process of dividing a fraction by a mixed number compare with our previous work with division of fractions? Discuss similarities and differences.
  - *Answers will vary, but some possibilities are listed below.*

    Similarities: We can use the invert and multiply method for both types of problems.

    Differences: It is necessary to change the mixed number into a fraction greater than one before applying the invert and multiply method.

Exit Ticket (4 minutes)

Lesson 8:   Dividing Fractions and Mixed Numbers

EUREKA
MATH

Name _____   Date _____

Lesson 8: Dividing Fractions and Mixed Numbers

Exit Ticket

Calculate the quotient.

1. $\dfrac{3}{4} \div 5\dfrac{1}{5}$

2. $\dfrac{3}{7} \div 2\dfrac{1}{2}$

3. $\dfrac{5}{8} \div 6\dfrac{5}{6}$

4. $\dfrac{5}{8} \div 8\dfrac{3}{10}$

© 2015 Great Minds. eureka-math.org
G6-M2-TE-B2-1.3.1-01.2016

Exit Ticket Sample Solutions

Calculate the quotient.

1. $\frac{3}{4} \div 5\frac{1}{5}$

   $\frac{3}{4} \div 5\frac{1}{5} = \frac{3}{4} \div \frac{26}{5} = \frac{3}{4} \times \frac{5}{26} = \frac{15}{104}$

2. $\frac{3}{7} \div 2\frac{1}{2}$

   $\frac{3}{7} \div 2\frac{1}{2} = \frac{3}{7} \div \frac{5}{2} = \frac{3}{7} \times \frac{2}{5} = \frac{6}{35}$

3. $\frac{5}{8} \div 6\frac{5}{6}$

   $\frac{5}{8} \div 6\frac{5}{6} = \frac{5}{8} \div \frac{41}{6} = \frac{5}{8} \times \frac{6}{41} = \frac{30}{328}$ or $\frac{15}{164}$

4. $\frac{5}{8} \div 8\frac{3}{10}$

   $\frac{5}{8} \div 8\frac{3}{10} = \frac{5}{8} \div \frac{83}{10} = \frac{5}{8} \times \frac{10}{83} = \frac{50}{664}$ or $\frac{25}{332}$

Problem Set Sample Solutions

Calculate each quotient.

1. $\frac{2}{5} \div 3\frac{1}{10}$

   $\frac{2}{5} \div \frac{31}{10} = \frac{2}{5} \times \frac{10}{31} = \frac{20}{155}$ or $\frac{4}{31}$

2. $4\frac{1}{3} \div \frac{4}{7}$

   $\frac{13}{3} \div \frac{4}{7} = \frac{13}{3} \times \frac{7}{4} = \frac{91}{12}$ or $7\frac{7}{12}$

3. $3\frac{1}{6} \div \frac{9}{10}$

   $\frac{19}{6} \div \frac{9}{10} = \frac{19}{6} \times \frac{10}{9} = \frac{190}{54}$ or $\frac{95}{27}$ or $3\frac{28}{54}$ or $3\frac{14}{27}$

4. $\frac{5}{8} \div 2\frac{7}{12}$

   $\frac{5}{8} \div \frac{31}{12} = \frac{5}{8} \times \frac{12}{31} = \frac{60}{248}$ or $\frac{15}{62}$

© 2015 Great Minds. eureka-math.org
G6-M2-TE-B2-1.3.1-01.2016

EUREKA
MATH

Memory Game

A.		B.	
$\dfrac{3}{4} \div 6\dfrac{2}{3}$	$\dfrac{9}{80}$	$\dfrac{1}{3} \div 4\dfrac{3}{4}$	$\dfrac{4}{57}$
C.		D.	
$\dfrac{2}{5} \div 1\dfrac{7}{8}$	$\dfrac{16}{75}$	$7\dfrac{1}{2} \div \dfrac{5}{6}$	9
E.		F.	
$3\dfrac{4}{7} \div \dfrac{5}{8}$	$5\dfrac{5}{7}$	$5\dfrac{5}{8} \div \dfrac{9}{10}$	$6\dfrac{1}{4}$
G.		H.	
$\dfrac{1}{4} \div 10\dfrac{11}{12}$	$\dfrac{3}{131}$	$5\dfrac{3}{4} \div \dfrac{5}{9}$	$10\dfrac{7}{20}$
I.		J.	
$3\dfrac{1}{5} \div \dfrac{2}{3}$	$4\dfrac{4}{5}$	$\dfrac{3}{5} \div 3\dfrac{1}{7}$	$\dfrac{21}{110}$
K.		L.	
$\dfrac{10}{13} \div 2\dfrac{4}{7}$	$\dfrac{35}{117}$	$2\dfrac{1}{4} \div \dfrac{7}{8}$	$2\dfrac{4}{7}$

© 2015 Great Minds. eureka-math.org
G6-M2-TE-B2-1.3.1-01.2016

6
GRADE

Mathematics Curriculum

Topic B

Multi-Digit Decimal Operations—Adding, Subtracting, and Multiplying

6.NS.B.3

Focus Standard:	6.NS.B.3	Fluently add, subtract, multiply, and divide multi-digit decimals using the standard algorithm for each operation.
Instructional Days:	3	
Lesson 9:	Sums and Differences of Decimals (P)[1]	
Lesson 10:	The Distributive Property and the Products of Decimals (P)	
Lesson 11:	Fraction Multiplication and the Products of Decimals (E)	

Prior to division of decimals, students revisit all decimal operations in Topic B. Students have had extensive experience with decimal operations to the hundredths and thousandths (**5.NBT.B.7**), which prepares them to easily compute with more decimal places. Students begin by relating the first lesson in this topic to mixed numbers from the last lesson in Topic A. They find that sums and differences of large mixed numbers can be more efficiently determined by first converting to a decimal and then applying the standard algorithms (**6.NS.B.3**). Within decimal multiplication, students begin to practice the distributive property. Students use arrays and partial products to understand and apply the distributive property as they solve multiplication problems involving decimals. Place value enables students to determine the placement of the decimal point in products and recognize that the size of a product is relative to each factor. Students discover and use connections between fraction multiplication and decimal multiplication.

---

[1]Lesson Structure Key: **P**-Problem Set Lesson, **M**-Modeling Cycle Lesson, **E**-Exploration Lesson, **S**-Socratic Lesson

---

Lesson 9: Sums and Differences of Decimals

Student Outcomes

- Students relate decimals to mixed numbers and round addends, minuends, and subtrahends to whole numbers in order to predict reasonable answers.
- Students use their knowledge of adding and subtracting multi-digit numbers to find the sums and differences of decimals.
- Students understand the importance of place value and solve problems in real-world contexts.

Lesson Notes

Students gained knowledge of rounding decimals in Grade 5. Students have also acquired knowledge of all operations with fractions and decimals to the hundredths place in previous grades.

Classwork

Discussion (5 minutes)

It is important for students to understand the connection between adding and subtracting mixed numbers and adding and subtracting decimals.

- Can you describe circumstances when it would be easier to add and subtract mixed numbers by converting them to decimals first?
  - *When fractions have large denominators, it would be difficult to find common denominators in order to add or subtract.*
  - *When a problem is solved by regrouping, it may be easier to borrow from decimals than fractions.*
- How can estimation be used to help solve addition and subtraction problems with rational numbers?
  - *Using estimation can help predict reasonable answers. It is a way to check to see if an answer is reasonable or not.*

Example 1 (8 minutes)

Use this example to show students how rounding addends, minuends, and subtrahends can help predict reasonable answers. Also, have students practice using correct vocabulary (addends, sum, minuends, subtrahends, and difference) when talking about different parts of the expressions.

MP.6

> **Example 1**
>
> $$25\frac{3}{10} + 376\frac{77}{100}$$

© 2015 Great Minds. eureka-math.org
G6-M2-TE-B2-1.3.1-01.2016

- Convert the mixed numbers into decimals.
  - $25.3 + 376.77$
- Round the addends to the nearest whole number. Then, find the estimated sum.
  - $25 + 377 = 402$
- Line up the addends appropriately using place value, and add.
  - $$\begin{array}{r} 25.3 \\ + 376.77 \\ \hline 402.07 \end{array}$$

Show students that the sum is close to the estimation. Also, show how the place value is important by completing the problem without lining up the place values. If this mistake is made, the actual sum is not close to the estimated sum.

Example 2 (8 minutes)

This example is used to show that changing mixed numbers into decimals may be the best choice to solve a problem.

Divide the class in half. Have students solve the same problem, with one-half of the class solving the problem using fractions and the other half of the class solving using decimals. Encourage students to estimate their answers before completing the problem.

> **Example 2**
>
> $426\dfrac{1}{5} - 275\dfrac{1}{2}$

Each group should get the same value as their answer; however, the fraction group has $150\dfrac{7}{10}$, and the decimal group has 150.7.

It is important for students to see that these numbers have the same value. Students solving the problem using fractions most likely take longer to solve the problem and make more mistakes. Point out to students that the answers represent the same value, but using decimals made the problem easier to solve.

When discussing the problem, use the correct vocabulary. $426\dfrac{1}{5}$ is the minuend, $275\dfrac{1}{2}$ is the subtrahend, and $150\dfrac{7}{10}$ is the difference.

EUREKA MATH

Exercises (14 minutes)

Students may work in pairs or individually to complete the following problems. Encourage students to write an expression and then round the addends, minuends, and subtrahends to the nearest whole number in order to predict a reasonable answer. Also, remind students that it is not always easier to change fractions to decimals before finding the sum or difference. Discuss the use of the approximation symbol when rounding decimals that repeat.

Exercises

Calculate each sum or difference.

1. Samantha and her friends are going on a road trip that is $245\frac{7}{50}$ miles long. They have already driven $128\frac{53}{100}$. How much farther do they have to drive?

   Expression: $245\frac{7}{50} - 128\frac{53}{100}$ *Estimated answer:* $245 - 129 = 116$

   Actual answer: $245.14 - 128.53 = 116.61$

2. Ben needs to replace two sides of his fence. One side is $367\frac{9}{100}$ meters long, and the other is $329\frac{3}{10}$ meters long. How much fence does Ben need to buy?

   Expression: $367\frac{9}{100} + 329\frac{3}{10}$ *Estimated answer:* $367 + 329 = 696$

   Actual answer: $367.09 + 329.3 = 696.39$

3. Mike wants to paint his new office with two different colors. If he needs $4\frac{4}{5}$ gallons of red paint and $3\frac{1}{10}$ gallons of brown paint, how much paint does he need in total?

   This problem is an example of where it may not be easiest to convert mixed numbers into decimals. Either method would result in a correct answer, but discuss with students why it may just be easier to find the sum by keeping the addends as mixed numbers.

   Expression: $4\frac{4}{5} + 3\frac{1}{10}$ *Estimated answer:* $5 + 3 = 8$

   Actual answer: $4\frac{8}{10} + 3\frac{1}{10} = 7\frac{9}{10}$

4. After Arianna completed some work, she figured she still had $78\frac{21}{100}$ pictures to paint. If she completed another $34\frac{23}{25}$ pictures, how many pictures does Arianna still have to paint?

   Expression: $78\frac{21}{100} - 34\frac{23}{25}$ *Estimated answer:* $78 - 35 = 43$

   Actual answer: $78.21 - 34.92 = 43.29$

   Use a calculator to convert the fractions into decimals before calculating the sum or difference.

5. Rahzel wants to determine how much gasoline he and his wife use in a month. He calculated that he used $78\frac{1}{3}$ gallons of gas last month. Rahzel's wife used $41\frac{3}{8}$ gallons of gas last month. How much total gas did Rahzel and his wife use last month? Round your answer to the nearest hundredth.

   Expression: $78\frac{1}{3} + 41\frac{3}{8}$ *Estimated answer:* $78 + 41 = 119$

   Actual answer: $78.333 + 41.375 \approx 119.71$

Closing (5 minutes)

- Have students share their answers and processes for each of the exercise problems.
- Discuss which exercises would be easiest if the addends, minuends, or subtrahends were converted to decimals.
  - *Exercises 1, 2, and 4 would be easiest if the terms were converted to decimals before finding the sum or difference.*
  - *The only way to calculate the exact sum for Exercise 5 would be to leave it as a fraction. However, it would be easiest to solve by converting the mixed numbers to decimals.*

Exit Ticket (5 minutes)

Lesson 9:   Sums and Differences of Decimals

Name _____ Date _____

Lesson 9: Sums and Differences of Decimals

Exit Ticket

Solve each problem. Show that the placement of the decimal is correct through either estimation or fraction calculation.

1. $382\frac{3}{10} - 191\frac{87}{100}$

2. $594\frac{7}{25} + 89\frac{37}{100}$

Exit Ticket Sample Solutions

Solve each problem. Show that the placement of the decimal is correct through either estimation or fraction calculation.

1. $382\frac{3}{10} - 191\frac{87}{100}$

    Estimation: $382 - 192 = 190$

    $382.3 - 191.87 = 190.43$

2. $594\frac{7}{25} + 89\frac{37}{100}$

    Estimation: $594 + 89 = 683$

    $594.28 + 89.37 = 683.65$

Problem Set Sample Solutions

1. Find each sum or difference.

    a. $381\frac{1}{10} - 214\frac{43}{100}$

        $381.1 - 214.43 = 166.67$

    b. $32\frac{3}{4} - 12\frac{1}{2}$

        $32\frac{3}{4} - 12\frac{2}{2} = 20\frac{1}{4}$ *or* 20.25

    c. $517\frac{37}{50} + 312\frac{3}{100}$

        $517.74 + 312.03 = 829.77$

    d. $632\frac{16}{25} + 32\frac{3}{10}$

        $632.64 + 32.3 = 664.94$

    e. $421\frac{3}{50} - 212\frac{9}{10}$

        $421.06 - 212.9 = 208.16$

2. Use a calculator to find each sum or difference. Round your answer to the nearest hundredth.

    a. $422\frac{3}{7} - 367\frac{5}{9}$

        $422.428571 - 367.555556 \approx 54.87$

    b. $23\frac{1}{5} + 45\frac{7}{8}$

        $23.2 + 45.875 \approx 69.08$

EUREKA MATH

Lesson 10: The Distributive Property and the Products of Decimals

Student Outcomes

- Through the use of arrays and partial products, students use place value and apply the distributive property to find the product of decimals.

Lesson Notes

Stations are used in this lesson. Therefore, some prep work needs to be completed. Prepare stations before class, and have a stopwatch available.

Classwork

Opening Exercise (3 minutes)

The Opening Exercise should be solved using the multiplication of decimals algorithm. These problems are revisited in Examples 1 and 2 to show how partial products can assist in finding the product of decimals.

Opening Exercise

Calculate the product.

    a. 200×32.6 b. 500×22.12

        $6,520$ $11,060$

Example 1 (5 minutes): Introduction to Partial Products

Show students how the distributive property can assist in calculating the product of decimals. Use this example to model the process.

Example 1: Introduction to Partial Products

Use partial products and the distributive property to calculate the product.

200×32.6

$200(32) + 200(0.6) = 6,400 + 120 = 6,520$

MP.7

Separate 32.6 into an addition expression with two addends, 32 and 0.6. Emphasize the importance of the place value. The problem is now $200 \times (32 + 0.6)$.

When the distributive property is applied, the problem is $200(32) + 200(0.6)$.

© 2015 Great Minds. eureka-math.org
G6-M2-TE-B2-1.3.1-01.2016

MP.7

It is ideal for students to to be able to solve these problems mentally using the distributive property, but it is understandable if additional scaffolding is needed for struggling students. Remind students that they need to complete the multiplication before adding. After giving students time to solve the problem, ask for their solutions.

Show students that the answer to this example is the same as the Opening Exercise but that most of the calculations in this example could be completed mentally.

Example 2 (7 minutes): Introduction to Partial Products

Have students try to calculate the product by using partial products. After they complete the problem, encourage students to check their answers by comparing it to the product of the second problem in the Opening Exercise. When a majority of the class has completed the problem, have some students share the processes they used to find the product. Answer all student questions before moving on to the exercises.

> **Scaffolding:**
> Possible extension: Have students complete more than two partial products. An example would be $500(20 + 2 + 0.1 + 0.02)$.

Example 2: Introduction to Partial Products

Use partial products and the distributive property to calculate the area of the rectangular patio shown below.

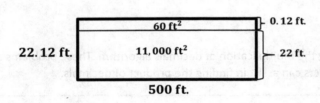

$$500 \times 22.12 = 500(22 + 0.12) = 500(22) + 500(0.12) = 11,000 + 60 = 11,060$$

The area of the patio would be $11,060$ *square feet.*

Exercises (20 minutes)

Students complete stations individually or in pairs. Encourage students to use partial products in order to solve the problems. Students are to write the problem and their processes in the space provided in the student materials. Remind students to record each station in the correct place because not everyone starts at Station One.

MP.7

EUREKA
MATH

Exercises

Use the boxes below to show your work for each station. Make sure that you are putting the solution for each station in the correct box.

Station One:
Calculate the product of 300×25.4.
$300(25) + 300(0.4) = 7,500 + 120 = 7,620$
Station Two:
Calculate the product of 45.9×100.
$100(45) + 100(0.9) = 4,500 + 90 = 4,590$
Station Three:
Calculate the product of 800×12.3.
$800(12) + 800(0.3) = 9,600 + 240 = 9,840$
Station Four:
Calculate the product of 400×21.8.
$400(21) + 400(0.8) = 8,400 + 320 = 8,720$
Station Five:
Calculate the product of 32.6×200.
$200(32) + 200(0.6) = 6,400 + 120 = 6,520$

Closing (6 minutes)

Students share their answers to the stations and ask any unanswered questions.

Exit Ticket (4 minutes)

Name _____   Date _____

Lesson 10: The Distributive Property and the Products of Decimals

Exit Ticket

Complete the problem using partial products.

500×12.7

EUREKA MATH

Exit Ticket Sample Solutions

Complete the problem using partial products.

500×12.7

$500 \times 12.7 = 500(12) + 500(0.7) = 6,000 + 350 = 6,350$

Problem Set Sample Solutions

Calculate the product using partial products.

1. 400×45.2

   $400(45) + 400(0.2) = 18,000 + 80 = 18,080$

2. 14.9×100

   $100(14) + 100(0.9) = 1,400 + 90 = 1,490$

3. 200×38.4

   $200(38) + 200(0.4) = 7,600 + 80 = 7,680$

4. 900×20.7

   $900(20) + 900(0.7) = 18,000 + 630 = 18,630$

5. 76.2×200

   $200(76) + 200(0.2) = 15,200 + 40 = 15,240$

Lesson 11: Fraction Multiplication and the Products of Decimals

Student Outcomes

- Students use estimation and place value to determine the placement of the decimal point in products and to determine that the size of the product is relative to each factor.
- Students discover and use connections between fraction multiplication and decimal multiplication.
- Students recognize that the sum of the number of decimal digits in the factors yields the decimal digits in the product.

Lesson Notes

To complete this lesson, students need large poster paper and markers so that they can present their detailed solutions to the Exploratory Challenge.

Classwork

Exploratory Challenge (20 minutes)

Students work in small groups to complete the two given problems. After finding each product, group members use previous knowledge to convince their classmates that the product has the decimal in the correct location.

MP.1
MP.6
&
MP.7

- Students solve their problems on poster paper using the markers provided.
- On the poster paper, students include all work that supports their solutions and the placement of the decimal in the answer. Students may need to be prompted about their previous work with rounding and multiplication of mixed numbers.
- All groups, even those whose solutions or supporting work contains errors, present their solutions and explain their supporting work. Having the decimal in the wrong place allows for a discussion on why the decimal placement is incorrect. Since all groups are presenting, allow each group to present only one method of proving where the decimal should be placed.

© 2015 Great Minds. eureka-math.org
G6-M2-TE-B2-1.3.1-01.2016

Exploratory Challenge

You not only need to solve each problem, but your groups also need to prove to the class that the decimal in the product is located in the correct place. As a group, you are expected to present your informal proof to the class.

a. Calculate the product. 34.62×12.8

$$34.62 \times 12.8 = 443.136$$

Some possible proofs:

Using estimation: $35 \times 13 = 455$ *If the decimal was located in a different place, the product would not be close to* 455.

Using fractions: $34\frac{62}{100} \times 12\frac{8}{10} = \frac{3,462}{100} \times \frac{128}{10} = \frac{443,136}{1,000}$ *Because the denominator is* $1,000$, *the last digit should be in the thousandths place when writing the fraction as a decimal. Therefore, the answer would be* 443.136.

b. Xavier earns $\$11.50$ per hour working at the nearby grocery store. Last week, Xavier worked 13.5 hours. How much money did Xavier earn last week? Remember to round to the nearest penny.

$$11.5 \times 13.5 = 155.25$$

Some possible proofs:

Using estimation: $12 \times 14 = 168$ *If the decimal was located in a different place, the product would not be close to* 168.

Using fractions: $11\frac{5}{10} \times 13\frac{5}{10} = \frac{115}{10} \times \frac{135}{10} = \frac{15,525}{100}$ *Because the denominator is* 100, *the last digit should be in the hundredths place when writing the fraction as a decimal. Therefore, the answer would be* $\$155.25$.

Discussion (5 minutes)

- Do you see a connection between the number of decimal digits in the factors and the product?
  - *In the first problem, there are two decimal digits in the first factor and one decimal digit in the second factor, which is a total of three decimal digits. The product has three decimal digits.*
  - *In the second problem, both factors have one decimal digit for a total of two decimal digits in the factors. The product also has two decimal digits.*

Show students that this is another way to determine if their decimal points are in the correct place. If this point was brought up by students in their presentations, the discussion can reiterate this method to find the correct placement of the decimal. Remind students to place the decimal before eliminating any unnecessary zeros from the answer.

At the end of the discussion, have students record notes on decimal placement in the student materials.

Discussion

Record notes from the Discussion in the box below.

Lesson 11: Fraction Multiplication and the Products of Decimals

MP.6

Exercises (10 minutes)

Students work individually to solve the four practice problems. Emphasize the importance of decimal placement to hold place value.

Exercises

1. **Calculate the product.** 324.56×54.82

    $324.56 \times 54.82 = 17,792.3792$

2. **Kevin spends \$11.25 on lunch every week during the school year. If there are 35.5 weeks during the school year, how much does Kevin spend on lunch over the entire school year? Remember to round to the nearest penny.**

    $11.25 \times 35.5 = 399.375 \approx 399.38$

    Kevin would spend \$399.38 on lunch over the entire school year.

3. **Gunnar's car gets 22.4 miles per gallon, and his gas tank can hold 17.82 gallons of gas. How many miles can Gunnar travel if he uses all of the gas in the gas tank?**

    $22.4 \times 17.82 = 399.168$

    Gunnar can drive 399.168 miles on an entire tank of gas.

4. **The principal of East High School wants to buy a new cover for the sand pit used in the long-jump competition. He measured the sand pit and found that the length is 29.2 feet and the width is 9.8 feet. What will the area of the new cover be?**

    $29.2 \times 9.8 = 286.16$

    The cover should have an area of 286.16 square feet.

Closing (5 minutes)

- How can we use information about the factors to determine the place value of the product and the number of decimal digits in the product?
    - *Calculate the sum of decimal digits in the factors. This sum represents the number of decimal digits in the product.*

Exit Ticket (5 minutes)

EUREKA MATH

Name _____   Date _____

Lesson 11: Fraction Multiplication and the Product of Decimals

Exit Ticket

Use estimation or fraction multiplication to determine if your answer is reasonable.

1.   Calculate the product. 78.93×32.45

2.   Paint costs $29.95 per gallon. Nikki needs 12.25 gallons to complete a painting project. How much will Nikki spend on paint? Remember to round to the nearest penny.

Exit Ticket Sample Solutions

Use estimation or fraction multiplication to determine if your answer is reasonable.

1. Calculate the product. 78.93×32.45

    $78.93 \times 32.45 = 2,561.2785$

2. Paint costs $29.95 per gallon. Nikki needs 12.25 gallons to complete a painting project. How much will Nikki spend on paint? Remember to round to the nearest penny.

    $29.95 \times 12.25 = 366.89$

    Nikki would spend $366.89 *on paint to complete her project.*

Problem Set Sample Solutions

Solve each problem. Remember to round to the nearest penny when necessary.

1. Calculate the product. 45.67×32.58

    $45.67 \times 32.58 = 1,487.9286$

2. Deprina buys a large cup of coffee for $4.70 on her way to work every day. If there are 24 workdays in the month, how much does Deprina spend on coffee throughout the entire month?

    $4.70 \times 24 = 112.80$

    Deprina would spend $112.80 *a month on coffee.*

3. Krego earns $2,456.75 every month. He also earns an extra $4.75 every time he sells a new gym membership. Last month, Krego sold 32 new gym memberships. How much money did Krego earn last month?

    $2,456.75 + (4.75 \times 32) = 2,608.75$

    Krego earned $2,608.75 *last month.*

4. Kendra just bought a new house and needs to buy new sod for her backyard. If the dimensions of her yard are 24.6 feet by 14.8 feet, what is the area of her yard?

    $24.6 \times 14.8 = 364.08$

    The area of Kendra's yard is 364.08 *square feet.*

EUREKA
MATH

Name _____   Date _____

1. Yasmine is having a birthday party with snacks and activities for her guests. At one table, five people are sharing three-quarters of a pizza. What equal-sized portion of the whole pizza will each of the five people receive?

   a. Use a model (e.g., picture, number line, or manipulative materials) to represent the quotient.

   b. Write a number sentence to represent the situation. Explain your reasoning.

   c. If three-quarters of the pizza provided 12 pieces to the table, how many pieces were in the pizza when it was full? Support your answer with models.

2. Yasmine needs to create invitations for the party. She has $\frac{3}{4}$ of an hour to make the invitations. It takes her $\frac{1}{12}$ of an hour to make each card. How many invitations can Yasmine create?

a. Use a number line to represent the quotient.

b. Draw a model to represent the quotient.

c. Compute the quotient without models. Show your work.

Module 2: Arithmetic Operations Including Division of Fractions

3. Yasmine is serving ice cream with the birthday cake at her party. She has purchased $19\frac{1}{2}$ pints of ice cream. She will serve $\frac{3}{4}$ of a pint to each guest.

   a.   How many guests can be served ice cream?

   b.   Will there be any ice cream left? Justify your answer.

4. L.B. Johnson Middle School held a track and field event during the school year. Miguel took part in a four-person shot put team. Shot put is a track and field event where athletes throw (or "put") a heavy sphere, called a "shot," as far as possible. To determine a team score, the distances of all team members are added. The team with the greatest score wins first place. The current winning team's final score at the shot put is 52.08 ft. Miguel's teammates threw the shot put the following distances: 12.26 ft., 12.82 ft., and 13.75 ft. Exactly how many feet will Miguel need to throw the shot put in order to tie the current first-place score? Show your work.

5. The sand pit for the long jump has a width of 2.75 meters and a length of 9.54 meters. Just in case it rains, the principal wants to cover the sand pit with a piece of plastic the night before the event. How many square meters of plastic will the principal need to cover the sand pit?

6. The chess club is selling drinks during the track and field event. The club purchased water, juice boxes, and pouches of lemonade for the event. They spent $138.52 on juice boxes and $75.00 on lemonade. The club purchased three cases of water. Each case of water costs $6.80. What is the total cost of the drinks?

Module 2: Arithmetic Operations Including Division of Fractions

© 2015 Great Minds. eureka-math.org
G6-M2-TE-B2-1.3.1-01.2016

EUREKA
MATH

A Progression Toward Mastery

Assessment Task Item		STEP 1 Missing or incorrect answer and little evidence of reasoning or application of mathematics to solve the problem.	STEP 2 Missing or incorrect answer but evidence of some reasoning or application of mathematics to solve the problem.	STEP 3 A correct answer with some evidence of reasoning or application of mathematics to solve the problem, OR an incorrect answer with substantial evidence of solid reasoning or application of mathematics to solve the problem.	STEP 4 A correct answer supported by substantial evidence of solid reasoning or application of mathematics to solve the problem.
1	**a** **6.NS.A.1**	Student response is incorrect and is not supported by a visual model. OR Student did not answer the question.	Student response is incorrect, but some evidence of reasoning is presented with a flawed visual model.	Student visual model is correct; however, the quotient of $\frac{3}{20}$ is not determined. OR Student response is correct, and the answer is supported with a visual model, but the model is inaccurate.	Student response is correct. The visual model is appropriate and supports the quotient of $\frac{3}{20}$. Student may have chosen to support the quotient with the use of more than one visual model.
	b **6.NS.A.1**	Student response is incorrect. OR Student did not answer the question.	Student response is incorrect, but a portion of the equation has reasoning. For example, student may have figured out to divide by five but did not multiply by $\frac{1}{5}$ to determine the quotient.	Student response is incorrect; however, the equation shows reasoning. The equation supports dividing by 5 and makes connection to multiplying by $\frac{1}{5}$ to determine the quotient of $\frac{3}{20}$, but the computation is incorrect.	Student response of $\frac{3}{20}$ is correct. The equation depicts the situation and makes connections between division and multiplication. All calculations are correct.

	c **6.NS.A.1**	Student response is incorrect. Student found the product of $\frac{3}{4} \times 12$ to arrive at 9 as the solution. OR Student response is incorrect and is not supported with visual models.	Student response of 16 pieces is correct but is not supported with visual models. OR Student response is incorrect with no support but shows general understanding of the equation.	Student response of 16 is correct. Student arrived at the answer using an equation but did not support reasoning with a model. OR Student calculation is incorrect, but visual models support reasoning.	Student response of 16 is correct. Student supported the solution with appropriate visual models and determined the amount of each portion in order to determine the full amount.
2	**a** **6.NS.A.1**	Student response is incorrect or missing. OR Student found the product of $\frac{3}{4} \times \frac{1}{12}$ to reach the response of $\frac{1}{16}$. A number line diagram does not support the response.	Student response is incorrect but depicts some reasoning in an incomplete number line diagram. OR Student response of 9 invitations is correct without a supporting number line diagram.	Student response of 9 invitations is correct. Reasoning is evident through the use of a number line diagram, but the response is in terms of time, such as $\frac{9}{12}$ or $\frac{3}{4}$ of an hour, and not in the number of cards. OR Student response is correct through the use of calculation but is not supported by the number line diagram.	Student response of 9 invitations is correct. Reasoning is evident through the depiction of an accurately designed number line diagram.
	b **6.NS.A.1**	Student response is incorrect or missing. OR Student computed the product of $\frac{3}{4} \times \frac{1}{2}$ to reach the response of $\frac{3}{8}$. No visual representation supports student response.	Student response is incorrect but depicts some reasoning in an incomplete visual model. OR Student response is correct, but reasoning is unclear through the misuse of a visual model.	Student response is correct. Reasoning is evident through the use of visual models, but the response is in terms of time, such as $\frac{9}{12}$ or $\frac{3}{4}$ of an hour, and not in the number of cards. OR Student response is correct through the use of calculation but is not supported by the visual model.	Student response of 9 invitations is correct. Reasoning is evident through the depiction of an accurately designed visual model.
	c **6.NS.A.1**	Student response is incorrect or missing. OR Student computed the product of the given fractions instead of determining the quotient.	Student response is correct but includes no computation to support reasoning.	Student response is correct. Student computed the quotient as 9 invitations but showed minimal computation.	Student response of 9 invitations is correct. Student demonstrated evidence of reasoning through concise application of an equation with accurate calculations.

| 3 | a

6.NS.A.1 | Student response is incorrect or missing. OR Student determined the product of $19\frac{1}{2}$ and $\frac{3}{4}$. | Student response is correct but shows no computation or reasoning. OR Student response is incorrect, but reasoning is evident through calculations. | Student response of 26 people is correct and represents some reasoning through calculation. OR Student response shows reasoning and application of mixed number conversion but includes errors in calculation. | Student response is correct. Reasoning is evident through correct mixed number conversion. The quotient of 26 people is determined using apparent understanding of factors. |
|---|---|---|---|---|---|
| | b

6.NS.A.1 | Student response is missing. | Student response is incorrect and does not depict understanding of whole and mixed numbers. | Student response correctly determines that there will be no leftover ice cream but is not supported with a clear understanding of whole and mixed numbers. | Student response is correct. Student explanation and reasoning include the understanding that a mixed number response will provide leftover ice cream where a whole number response would not. |
| 4 | 6.NS.B.3 | Student response is incorrect. Justification does not include adding the given throw distances and determining the difference of that sum and the distance needed to tie for first place. Student response may show only addition. | Student response is incorrect but attempts to determine the sum of the throw distances first and then the difference of the sum and the distance needed to tie first place. | Student response is incorrect due to slight miscalculations when adding or subtracting. It is evident that student understands the process of adding the decimals first and then subtracting the sum from the other team's final score. | Student response is correct. Student accurately determines the sum of the throw distances as 38.83 feet and the differences between that sum and the score needed to tie as 13.25 feet. It is evident that student understands the process of adding the decimals first and then subtracting the sum from the other team's final score. |
| 5 | 6.NS.B.3 | Student response is incorrect or missing. The response depicts the use of an incorrect operation, such as addition or subtraction. | Student response is incorrect. The response shows understanding of multi-digit numbers but lacks precision in place value, resulting in a product less than 3 or more than 262. | Student response of 26.235 square meters is correct but shows little to no reasoning that multiplication is the accurate operation to choose to find the area of plastic to cover the sand pit. | Student response is correct and shows complete understanding of place value. The response of 26.235 square meters includes a picture that depicts finding the area through multiplication of the length and width of the sand pit. |

| 6 | 6.NS.B.3 | Student response is incorrect or missing. The response disregards finding the total price of the water. | Student response is incorrect. Student finds the total price of the water only. | Student response is incorrect. Student finds the total price of the water and adds it to the price of the lemonade and juice but makes minor computation errors. | Student response is correct. Student finds the total price of the water to be $20.40 and accurately adds it to the price of the lemonade and juice to determine a total cost of $233.92. |

EUREKA
MATH

Name _____ Date _____

1. Yasmine is having a birthday party with snacks and activities for her guests. At one table, five people are sharing three-quarters of a pizza. What equal-sized portion of the pizza will each of the five people receive?

   a. Use a model (e. g., picture, number line, or manipulative materials) to represent the quotient.

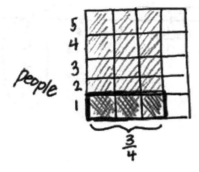

   b. Write a number sentence to represent the situation. Explain your reasoning.

   Because there are 5 people, we found 1 out of the 5, which is $\frac{1}{5}$. I can represent the situation as:

   $$\frac{3}{4} \div 5 = \frac{3}{4} \cdot \frac{1}{5} = \frac{3}{20}$$

   c. If three-quarters of the pizza provided 12 pieces to the table, how many pieces were in the pizza when it was full? Support your answer with models.

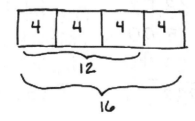

   $\frac{12}{3} = 4$, each portion is 4,

   $4 \cdot 4 = 16$ pieces

2. Yasmine needs to create invitations for the party. She has $\frac{3}{4}$ of an hour to make the invitations. It takes her $\frac{1}{12}$ of an hour to make each card. How many invitations can Yasmine create?

a. Use a number line to represent the quotient.

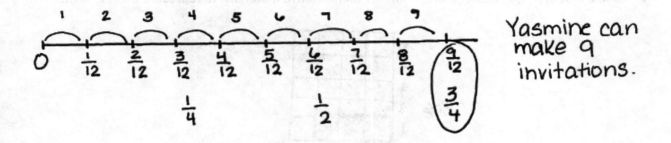

Yasmine can make 9 invitations.

b. Draw a model to represent the quotient.

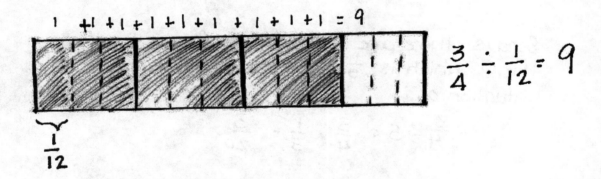

$$\frac{3}{4} \div \frac{1}{12} = 9$$

c. Compute the quotient without models. Show your work.

water   juice $138.52   The total
$6.80   lemonade $ 75.00   cost of the
×   3   water   +$ 20.40   drinks is
$20.40 $233.92 $233.92.

EUREKA MATH

© 2015 Great Minds. eureka-math.org
G6-M2-TE-B2-1.3.1-01.2016

3. Yasmine is serving ice cream with the birthday cake at her party. She has purchased $19\frac{1}{2}$ pints of ice cream. She will serve $\frac{3}{4}$ of a pint to each guest.

    a. How many guests can be served ice cream?

$$\begin{array}{r} 19 \\ \times\ 2 \\ \hline 38+1=39 \end{array}$$

$$19\tfrac{1}{2} \div \tfrac{3}{4}$$
$$\downarrow$$
$$\frac{39}{2} \div \frac{3}{4} = \frac{^{13}39}{2_1} \cdot \frac{\cancel{4}^{2}}{\cancel{3}_1} = 13 \times 2 = 26$$

Yasmine can serve 26 people.

    b. Will there be any ice cream left? Justify your answer.

My answer, 26, is a whole number, so there will be no ice cream left over. If my answer was 26 ¼ or any mixed number, there would be ice cream left over.

4. L.B. Johnson Middle School held a track and field event during the school year. Miguel took part in a four-person shot put team. Shot put is a track and field event where athletes throw (or "put") a heavy sphere, called a "shot," as far as possible. To determine a team score, the distances of all team members are added. The team with the greatest score wins first place. The current winning team's final score at the shot put is 52.08 ft. Miguel's teammates threw the shot put the following distances: 12.26 ft., 12.82 ft., and 13.75 ft. Exactly how many feet will Miguel need to throw the shot put in order to tie the current first-place score? Show your work.

$$\begin{array}{r} 12.26 \\ 12.82 \\ +\ 13.75 \\ \hline 38.83 \end{array}$$

$$\begin{array}{r} 52.08 \\ -\ 38.83 \\ \hline 13.25 \end{array}$$

Miguel will need to throw the shot put 13.25 feet to tie the current first place score.

5. The sand pit for the long jump has a width of 2.75 meters and a length of 9.54 meters. Just in case it rains, the principal wants to cover the sand pit with a piece of plastic the night before the event. How many square meters of plastic will the principal need to cover the sand pit?

$$
\begin{array}{r}
9.54 \\
\times\ 2.75 \\
\hline
4770 \\
67780 \\
+190800 \\
\hline
26.2350
\end{array}
$$

The principal needs 26.235 m² of plastic to cover the sand pit.

6. The chess club is selling drinks during the track and field event. The club purchased water, juice boxes, and pouches of lemonade for the event. They spent $138.52 on juice boxes and $75.00 on lemonade. The club purchased three cases of water. Each case of water costs $6.80. What is the total cost of the drinks?

water
$$
\begin{array}{r}
\$6.80 \\
\times\ \ \ \ 3 \\
\hline
\$20.40
\end{array}
$$

juice $138.52
lemonade $ 75.00
water   +$ 20.40
$$\overline{\hspace{2.5cm}}$$
            $233.92

The total cost of the drinks is $233.92.

EUREKA MATH

6
GRADE

Mathematics Curriculum

Topic C

Dividing Whole Numbers and Decimals

6.NS.B.2, 6.NS.B.3

Focus Standards:	6.NS.B.2	Fluently divide multi-digit numbers using the standard algorithm.
	6.NS.B.3	Fluently add, subtract, multiply, and divide multi-digit decimals using the standard algorithm for each operation.
Instructional Days:	4	
	Lesson 12:	Estimating Digits in a Quotient (P)[1]
	Lesson 13:	Dividing Multi-Digit Numbers Using the Algorithm (P)
	Lesson 14:	The Division Algorithm—Converting Decimal Division into Whole Number Division Using Fractions (P)
	Lesson 15:	The Division Algorithm—Converting Decimal Division into Whole Number Division Using Mental Math (P)

In Topic C, students build upon previous lessons to fluently divide numbers and decimals. They apply estimation to place value and determine that the standard algorithm is simply a tally system arranged in place value columns **(6.NS.B.2).** Students understand that when they "bring down" the next digit in the algorithm, they are distributing, recording, and shifting to the next place value. They understand that the steps in the algorithm continually provide better approximations to the answer. Students further their understanding of division as they develop fluency in the use of the standard algorithm to divide multi-digit decimals **(6.NS.B.3).** They make connections to division of fractions and rely on mental math strategies in order to implement the division algorithm when finding the quotients of decimals.

---

[1]Lesson Structure Key: **P**-Problem Set Lesson, **M**-Modeling Cycle Lesson, **E**-Exploration Lesson, **S**-Socratic Lesson

Lesson 12: Estimating Digits in a Quotient

Student Outcomes

- Students connect estimation with place value in order to determine the standard algorithm for division.

Lesson Notes

The goal of this lesson is to ultimately answer why estimation is useful. Estimation is the process of quickly finding an approximate answer to a given computation. Teaching estimation is an excellent way of extending place value concepts to large numbers and decimals. It helps to develop a sense of the relative sizes of numbers.

Students need prerequisite skills to transition from dividing by a single-digit divisor to a two-digit divisor. These skills include place value concepts for four- and five-digit numbers, multiplication by two-digit numbers, and estimating division by two-digit numbers. This lesson focuses on estimating division by two-digit numbers first by rounding to one-digit arithmetic facts. Students turn every estimate into one-digit facts and then overlay the division algorithm.

In previous grade levels, students have been introduced to a reformatted algorithm for multiplication. This algorithm is evident in the examples presented in this module. Below is a reference to follow when modeling the division algorithm with students.

In previous algorithms, students regrouped in the tens place when they multiplied 8 ones times 2 ones and found the product 16. They then continued multiplying 2 ones and 4 tens and then added that carried over ten (9 tens). This is sufficient for now. From there, they multiplied 3 tens and 8 ones and found 24 tens. This is where the problem occurs. Students have always placed the regrouped 2 in the tens place again after crossing out the original 1. This is wrong. That 2 represents 20 tens and should be placed in the *hundreds* place.

$$
\begin{array}{r}
\overset{2}{\overset{\cancel{1}}{}}\ 4\ 8 \\
\times\quad 3\ 2 \\
\hline
9\ 6 \\
+\ 1\ 4\ 4\ 0 \\
\hline
1\ 5\ 3\ 6
\end{array}
$$

This faulty algorithm is alleviated by placing the regrouped numbers in the correct place value. Below, the same problem shows the regrouped numbers in the correct place value.

$$
\begin{array}{r}
4\ 8 \\
\times\quad 3\ 2 \\
\hline
\cancel{1} \\
9\ 6 \\
\overset{\cancel{2}}{} \\
+\ 1\ 4\ 4\ 0 \\
\hline
1\ 5\ 3\ 6
\end{array}
$$

Students in previous grades have been responsible for correctly tallying numbers in their correct place values in the long division algorithm as well.

```
                    4   8
    3   2 │ 1   5   3   6
        −   1   2   8
                2   5   6
                    ̶1
            −   2   5   6
                        0
```

Here, the regrouped ten in the correct place value is evident when finding the product of 8 ones and 2 ones. The regrouped ten is clearly represented in the correct place value.

Classwork

Discussion (3 minutes)

Take this time to recall previously learned strategies and unit form. Display the following problem: Divide 150 by 30.

- How can we represent this problem using division notation?
  - $150 \div 30$
- Using the place value of ten, how can we represent this problem in a different way?
  - 15 *tens* ÷ 3 *tens*
- This is a problem that we can represent now as the following. (Display the problem.)

$$150 \div 30$$
$$150 \div 10 \div 3$$
$$15\overline{0} \div 3\overline{0}$$
$$15 \div 3$$

- What is the quotient of 15 and 3?
  - 5
- We can represent this using the division algorithm, too.

```
                    5
    3   0 │ 1   5   0
        −   1   5   0
                    0
```

- This information helps us estimate.

Discussion

Divide 150 by 30.

$$150 \div 30$$
$$150 \div 10 \div 3$$
$$150 \div \cancel{30}$$
$$15 \div 3$$

```
                    5
  3   0 | 1   5   0
      − 1   5   0
                0
```

Example 1 (5 minutes): Rounding to a One-Digit Arithmetic Fact

This example focuses on students fluently using rounding to efficiently estimate divisors, dividends, and quotients.
Display the problem:

```
  3   8 | 2   6   8   9   7
```

- Let's do some rounding to efficiently estimate the quotient here. What number can we round the divisor to?
  - *38 is close to* 40.
- What number can we round the dividend to that is easily divisible by 40?
  - *We can round the dividend to* 24,000.

Display the problem:

```
  4   0 | 2   4   0   0   0
```

- We have rounded in a way that now we can think of this problem as a one-digit arithmetic fact.

Display the problem:

```
  4 | 2   4   0   0
```

- We can also think of this as the following:

```
  4 | 2   4
```

- What is 24 divided by 4?
  - 6
- What is the quotient of $2,400 \div 4$?
  - 600
- What is the quotient of $24,000 \div 40$?
  - 600

EUREKA
MATH

- What a good estimate for $26{,}897 \div 38$?
  - 600
- Let's check it with a calculator. What is $26{,}897 \div 38$?
  - *Approximately* 707.82
- I would agree that our estimate is pretty accurate. It is in the same place value (hundreds).

Exercises 1–4 (10 minutes)

Students practice rounding and estimating to one-digit arithmetic facts. They notice the accuracy of rounding with divisors with 1, 2, 8, and 9 in the ones place.

Exercises 1–5

Round to estimate the quotient. Then, compute the quotient using a calculator, and compare the estimation to the quotient.

1. $2{,}970 \div 11$

    a. **Round to a one-digit arithmetic fact. Estimate the quotient.**

$$1\ 1\ \overline{|\ 2\quad 9\quad 7\quad 0}$$

$$1\ 0\ \overline{|\ 3\quad 0\quad 0\quad 0}$$

$$\overset{3}{1\ \overline{|\ 3}}$$

$$\overset{3\quad 0\quad 0}{1\ \overline{|\ 3\quad 0\quad 0}}$$

Estimate: **300**

    b. **Use a calculator to find the quotient. Compare the quotient to the estimate.**

    $2{,}970 \div 11 = 270$

    The quotient is very close to the estimate.

---

2. 4,752 ÷ 12

    a. **Round to a one-digit arithmetic fact. Estimate the quotient.**

```
1   2 | 4   7   5   2

1   0 | 5   0   0   0
```

```
        5
    1 | 5
```

```
        5   0   0
    1 | 5   0   0
```

Estimate: 500

    b. **Use a calculator to find the quotient. Compare the quotient to the estimate.**

    $4,752 ÷ 12 = 396$

    The quotient is close to the estimate but not as close as the estimate in the first exercise.

3. 11,647 ÷ 19

    a. **Round to a one-digit arithmetic fact. Estimate the quotient.**

```
1   9 | 1   1   6   4   7

2   0 | 1   2   0   0   0
```

```
            6
    2 | 1   2
```

```
            6   0   0
    2 | 1   2   0   0
```

Estimate: 600

    b. **Use a calculator to find the quotient. Compare the quotient to the estimate.**

    $11,647 ÷ 19 = 613$

    The quotient is very close to the estimate.

EUREKA MATH

4. 40,644 ÷ 18

    a.   **Round to a one-digit arithmetic fact. Estimate the quotient.**

$$1\ 8\ \overline{)\ 4\quad 0\quad 6\quad 4\quad 4}$$

$$2\ 0\ \overline{)\ 4\quad 0\quad 0\quad 0\quad 0}$$

$$2\ \overline{)\ 4}^{\ 2}$$

$$2\ \overline{)\ 4\quad 0\quad 0\quad 0}^{\ 2\quad 0\quad 0\quad 0}$$

Estimate: **2,000**

    b.   **Use a calculator to find the quotient. Compare the quotient to the estimate.**

       40,644 ÷ 18 = 2,258

       The quotient is close to the estimate but not as close as the estimate in the third exercise.

Example 2 (5 minutes): Estimates Further Away

Students should be seeing a pattern. The closer the divisor is to a multiple of 10, the more accurate the estimation of the quotient. In Exercises 1 and 3, students had divisors that were one number away from a multiple of 10 and their estimates of the quotients were very accurate. In Exercises 2 and 4, students were a bit further away from a multiple of 10. The estimates were still close to the quotients but not as accurate as when the divisor is closer to a multiple of 10. But, what happens when the quotient ends in 4, 5, or 6?

- Let's take a look at a division problem where the divisor has a 4 in the ones place.

Display the problem: $59,262 ÷ 14$.

- Let's make a conjecture about the accuracy of the estimate of the quotient. Do you think the estimate is as accurate as in the previous exercises?
  - *Student responses may vary but should support the notion that the further away a divisor is from a multiple of ten, the less accurate the estimate.*
- Let's round the divisor and the dividend. If we were to round the divisor to a multiple of 10, would you round 14 to 10 or to 20?
  - *Student responses may vary, but it is likely that students round* 14 *to* 10.
- How would we round the dividend?
  - 60,000

Display the problem:

$$1\ 0\ \overline{)\ 6\quad 0\quad 0\quad 0\quad 0}$$

- We have rounded in a way that now we can think of this problem as a one-digit arithmetic fact.

Display the problem:

$$1\,\overline{)\,6\quad 0\quad 0\quad 0}$$

- We can also think of this as the following:

$$1\,\overline{)\,6}$$

- What is 6 divided by 1?
  - 6
- What is the quotient of 6,000 ÷ 1?
  - 6,000
- What is the quotient of 60,000 ÷ 10?
  - 6,000
- What is a good estimate for 59,262 ÷ 14?
  - 6,000
- Let's check it with a calculator. What is 59,262 ÷ 14?
  - 4,233
- What are you noticing here? Can you see the continuation of a pattern?
  - *Student responses may vary. Students should continue to see that the estimated quotient is less accurate than those with divisors closer to a multiple of* 10.

Exercise 5 (3 minutes)

Students practice rounding and estimating to one-digit arithmetic facts. They notice that when dividing by a divisor with a 5 in the ones place, the estimated quotient is less accurate.

---

5. **49,170 ÷ 15**

    a. **Round to a one-digit arithmetic fact. Estimate the quotient.**

$$1\;5\,\overline{)\,4\quad 9\quad 1\quad 7\quad 0}\qquad\qquad or\qquad\qquad 1\;5\,\overline{)\,4\quad 9\quad 1\quad 7\quad 0}$$

$$1\;0\,\overline{)\,5\quad 0\quad 0\quad 0\quad 0}\qquad\qquad\qquad\qquad 2\;0\,\overline{)\,4\quad 0\quad 0\quad 0\quad 0}$$

$$\overset{5}{1\,\overline{)\,5}}\qquad\qquad\qquad\qquad\qquad\qquad \overset{2}{2\,\overline{)\,4}}$$

$$\overset{5\quad 0\quad 0\quad 0}{1\,\overline{)\,5\quad 0\quad 0\quad 0}}\qquad\qquad\qquad\qquad \overset{2\quad 0\quad 0\quad 0}{2\,\overline{)\,4\quad 0\quad 0\quad 0}}$$

Estimates may vary but could include **5,000** *or* **2,000.**

Lesson 12:   Estimating Digits in a Quotient

EUREKA MATH

---

b. **Use a calculator to find the quotient. Compare the quotient to the estimate.**

49,170 ÷ 15 = 3,278

The quotient is somewhat close to the estimate; however, it is not as accurate as previous exercises and examples where the divisors were closer to a multiple of 10.

Example 3 (9 minutes): Extend Estimation and Place Value to the Division Algorithm

Extend estimation and place value to the division algorithm. The purpose of this example is to bridge estimation of quotients to estimation of digits in a quotient.

- Let's take a look at 918 ÷ 27. How can we estimate using place value similar to the previous problems?
  - 900 ÷ 30, *or* 90 *tens divided by* 3 *tens. (Answers may vary but should be consistent with students utilizing place value to assist in efficient estimation.)*

- We can rewrite this as: (display)

$$2 \ 7 \ \overline{)\ 9 \ \ 1 \ \ 8}$$

$$3 \ 0 \ \overline{)\ 9 \ \ 0 \ \ 0}$$

$$\overset{3}{3 \ \overline{)\ 9}}$$

$$\overset{3 \quad 0}{3 \ \overline{)\ 9 \ \ 0 \ \ 0}}$$

- What is the quotient of 90 ÷ 3?
  - 30

- We can conclude that a good estimation for the quotient of 918 ÷ 27 is 30.

- Let's apply our estimation to the division algorithm.

- How many times can 27 ones go into 918 ones?
  - 3 × 27 = 81; 30 *times*

- Record 3 in the tens place (stands for 3 tens). We record the 1 in the tens place and the 8 in the hundreds place because we know 81 tens is the same as 810. Find the remainder in the tens place.
  - 91 tens − 81 tens = 10 tens

- Can we divide 10 tens by 27?
  - *We must regroup first.*

- We need to regroup these 10 tens into 100 ones and combine with the 8 already in the ones place. What does the remainder 108 represent?
  - 108 *ones*

$$\begin{array}{r} 3 \\ 2\ 7\ \overline{\smash{)}\ 9\ \ 1\ \ 8} \\ \underline{-\ \ \ 8\ \ 1 } \\ 1\ \ 0\ \ 8 \end{array}$$

$$\begin{array}{r} 3\ \ 4 \\ 2\ 7\ \overline{\smash{)}\ 9\ \ 1\ \ 8} \\ \underline{-\ \ \ 8\ \ 1 } \\ 1\ \ 0\ \ 8 \\ \underline{-\ \ 1\ \ 0\ \ 8} \\ 0 \end{array}$$

- Here we have 108 ones ÷ 27 ones. Let's estimate again.
    - $100 \div 25 = 4$
- What is the product of 27×4?
    - 108
- Record 108 in the ones place and subtract.
    - $108 - 108 = 0$
- We have no remainder. What is the quotient of $918 \div 27$?
    - 34
- Multiply 27×34 to check.
    - $27 \times 34 = 918$
- Is our quotient, 34, close to our estimation, 30?
    - *Yes*

Example 3

Estimate and apply the division algorithm to evaluate the expression $918 \div 27$.

Estimate:

$918 \div 27$

$900 \div 30$

$90 \ tens \div 3 \ tens$

$900 \div 30$

$90 \div 3 = 30$

$$\begin{array}{r} 3 \quad 4 \\ 2 \ 7 \overline{)\ 9 \quad 1 \quad 8} \\ 2 \\ -\underline{8 \quad 1} \\ 1 \quad 0 \quad 8 \\ 2 \\ -\underline{1 \quad 0 \quad 8} \\ 0 \end{array}$$

$27 \times 30 = 810$

$108 \div 27$

$100 \ ones \div 25 \ ones$

$100 \div 25 = 4$

$27 \times 4 = 108$

$918 \div 27 = 34$

Closing (5 minutes)

- What is the benefit of estimating before we divide?
    - *Rounding to a one-digit arithmetic fact allows us to determine an approximate quotient. We use approximate quotients to determine reasonableness of our calculations.*
- What did you notice about divisors that are closer to multiples of ten?
    - *The closer the divisor is to a multiple of ten, the more accurate the estimate.*
- What is problematic with divisors with the digits 4, 5, and 6 in the ones place?
    - *Divisors with digits 4, 5, and 6 in the ones place have less accurate estimates.*
- We see in upcoming lessons that although these are less accurate estimates, we can use other mental math strategies to assist us when dividing. Brainstorm with a partner to discuss other mental math strategies that could help us divide efficiently while still estimating.

Exit Ticket (5 minutes)

Lesson 12:   Estimating Digits in a Quotient

EUREKA MATH

Name _____   Date _____

Lesson 12: Estimating Digits in a Quotient

Exit Ticket

Round to estimate the quotient. Then, compute the quotient using a calculator, and compare the estimation to the quotient.

1. $4,732 \div 13$

2. $22,752 \div 16$

Exit Ticket Sample Solutions

> Round to estimate the quotient. Then, compute the quotient using a calculator, and compare the estimation to the quotient.

1. $4,732 \div 13$

   Answers may vary.

   $$1 \quad 0 \overline{)\; 5 \quad 0 \quad 0 \quad 0}$$

   $$5$$
   $$1 \overline{)\; 5}$$

   $$5 \quad 0 \quad 0$$
   $$1 \overline{)\; 5 \quad 0 \quad 0}$$

   Estimate: 500

   $4,732 \div 13 = 364$

   The quotient 364 *is somewhat close to the estimate. Both numbers are in the hundreds. If the divisor was closer to a multiple of* 10, *the estimate would have been closer to the quotient.*

2. $22,752 \div 16$

   $$2 \quad 0 \overline{)\; 2 \quad 0 \quad 0 \quad 0 \quad 0}$$

   $$1$$
   $$2 \overline{)\; 2}$$

   $$1 \quad 0 \quad 0 \quad 0$$
   $$2 \overline{)\; 2 \quad 0 \quad 0 \quad 0}$$

   Estimate: 1,000

   $22,752 \div 16 = 1,422$

   The quotient $1,422$ *is somewhat close to the estimate. Both numbers are in the thousands place. The quotient is almost* 1.5 *times the estimate. The estimate would have been much closer to the quotient had the divisor been closer to a multiple of* 10.

EUREKA
MATH

Problem Set Sample Solutions

> **Round to estimate the quotient. Then, compute the quotient using a calculator, and compare the estimate to the quotient.**
>
> *Estimates may vary.*
>
> 1. $715 \div 11$
>
>   *Estimate:* $700 \div 10 = 70$
>
>   *Quotient:* $715 \div 11 = 65$
>
>   *Comparison: Since the dividend is very close to a multiple of ten, the quotient is very close to the estimate.*
>
> 2. $7,884 \div 12$
>
>   *Estimate:* $8,000 \div 10 = 800$
>
>   *Quotient:* $7,884 \div 12 = 657$
>
>   *Comparison: The dividend is close to a multiple of ten, so the quotient is close to the estimate.*
>
> 3. $9,646 \div 13$
>
>   *Estimate:* $10,000 \div 10 = 1,000$
>
>   *Quotient:* $9,646 \div 13 = 742$
>
>   *Comparison: The dividend is somewhat close to a multiple of ten, so the quotient is fairly close to the estimate.*
>
> 4. $11,942 \div 14$
>
>   *Estimate:* $12,000 \div 10 = 1,200$
>
>   *Quotient:* $11,942 \div 14 = 853$
>
>   *Comparison: The dividend is not as close to a multiple of ten, so the quotient is not nearly as close to the estimate as dividends that are closer to a multiple of ten.*
>
> 5. $48,825 \div 15$
>
>   *Estimate:* $50,000 \div 10 = 5,000$
>
>   *Quotient:* $48,825 \div 15 = 3,255$
>
>   *Comparison: The dividend is midway between multiples of ten. The quotient is in the same place value but is not as close to the estimate as dividends that are closer to a multiple of ten.*
>
> 6. $135,296 \div 16$
>
>   *Estimate:* $140,000 \div 20 = 7,000$
>
>   *Quotient:* $135,296 \div 16 = 8,456$
>
>   *Comparison: The dividend is not as close to a multiple of ten, so the quotient is not nearly as close to the estimate as dividends that are closer to a multiple of ten.*

7. $199,988 \div 17$

   Estimate: $200,000 \div 20 = 10,000$

   Quotient: $199,998 \div 17 = 11,764$

   Comparison: The dividend is somewhat close to a multiple of ten, so the quotient is fairly close to the estimate.

8. $116,478 \div 18$

   Estimate: $120,000 \div 20 = 6,000$

   Quotient: $116,478 \div 18 = 6,471$

   Comparison: The dividend is close to a multiple of ten, so the quotient is close to the estimate.

9. $99,066 \div 19$

   Estimate: $100,000 \div 20 = 5,000$

   Quotient: $99,066 \div 19 = 5,214$

   Comparison: Since the dividend is very close to a multiple of ten, the quotient is very close to the estimate.

10. $181,800 \div 20$

    Estimate: $180,000 \div 20 = 9,000$

    Quotient: $181,800 \div 20 = 9,090$

    Comparison: Since the divisor is a multiple of ten, the quotient is almost exactly the same as the estimate.

Lesson 12:   Estimating Digits in a Quotient

EUREKA MATH®

Lesson 13: Dividing Multi-Digit Numbers Using the Algorithm

Student Outcomes

- Students understand that the standard algorithm of division is simply a tally system arranged in place value columns.

Classwork

Example 1 (10 minutes)

Students estimate, make a table of values, and use place value to divide multi-digit numbers using the division algorithm.

Display the expression $70,072 \div 19$.

- Let's first estimate the quotient. Look at the dividend. To what number could 70,072 be rounded?
  - □ *Student response may vary but should represent an efficient number to compute the estimation.* 70,000
- Look at the divisor. To what number can 19 be rounded?
  - □ *Student response may vary but should reflect work done in Lesson 12 where students discovered estimates of quotients are most accurate the closer the dividend is to a multiple of* 10. 20
- Let's divide 70,000 by 20. Display the following:

$$70,000 \div 20$$

- Divide each number by ten for efficiency. Display the following:

$$70,000 \div 20$$
$$70,000 \div 10 \div 2$$
$$7,000 \div 2 = 3,500$$

Example 1

Divide $70,072 \div 19$.

    a.   **Estimate:**

$$70,000 \div 20$$
$$70,000 \div 10 \div 2$$
$$7,000 \div 2 = 3,500$$

- The quotient of 70,072 and 19 should be about 3,500.
- Because the divisor, 19, is not a friendly number, a good strategy is to create a table of values to show the multiples of 19.

Elicit responses to complete the table of values.

> **b.   Create a table to show the multiples of 19.**
>
> | Multiples of 19 |
> | --- |
> | $1 \times 19 = 19$ |
> | $2 \times 19 = 38$ |
> | $3 \times 19 = 57$ |
> | $4 \times 19 = 76$ |
> | $5 \times 19 = 95$ |
> | $6 \times 19 = 114$ |
> | $7 \times 19 = 133$ |
> | $8 \times 19 = 152$ |
> | $9 \times 19 = 171$ |

- Let's use the table of multiples of 19 to assist us when dividing.
- Can we divide 70 thousands into 19 groups or into groups of 19?
  - *Yes*
- How can you estimate to divide 70 by 19?
  - *We could round the dividend to 60 and the divisor to 20. $60 \div 20 = 3$.*
- Using this estimation and the table of multiples, how many times does 19 go into 70 thousands?
  - *$3 \times 19 = 57$; 3,000 times*
- Record 3 in the thousands place. We record the 5 in the ten thousands place and the 7 in the thousands place because we know 57 thousands is the same as 57,000. Find the remainder in the thousands place.
  - *$70 - 57 = 13$*
- Can we divide 13 thousands by 19?
  - *We must regroup first.*
- We need to regroup these 13 thousands into 130 hundreds.
- How many times does 19 go into 130 hundreds?
  - *$6 \times 19 = 114$; 600 times*
- Record 6 in the hundreds place, and find the remainder in the hundreds place.
  - *$130 - 114 = 16$*

Lesson 13:   Dividing Multi-Digit Numbers Using the Algorithm

EUREKA MATH

- Can we divide 16 hundreds by 19?
  - *We must regroup first.*
- We need to regroup these 16 hundreds and combine with the 7 already in the tens place. What does the remainder 167 represent?
  - 167 *tens*
- Can we divide 167 tens by 19? How many times does 19 go into 167 tens?
  - $8 \times 19 = 152$; 80 *times*
- Record 8 in the tens place, and find the remainder.
  - $167 - 152 = 15$ *tens*
- Can we divide 15 tens by 19?
  - *We must regroup first.*
- We need to regroup these 15 tens and combine with the 2 already in the ones place. What does the remainder 152 represent?
  - 152 *ones*
- How many times does 19 go into 152 ones?
  - $8 \times 19 = 152$; 8 *times*
- Place 8 in the ones place, and find the remainder.
  - $152 - 152 = 0$

```
                  3  6  8  8
         1  9 │ 7  0  0  7  2
                  2
              -   5  7
                  1  3  0
                     5
              -   1  1  4
                     1  6  7
                        7
              -      1  5  2
                        1  5  2
                           7
              -         1  5  2
                              0
```

---

c. Use the algorithm to divide 70,072 ÷ 19. Check your work.

```
                  3  6  8  8
         1  9 │ 7  0  0  7  2
                  2
              -   5  7                        3  6  8  8
                  1  3  0                  ×     1  9
                     5                        6  7  7
              -   1  1  4            3  3  1  9  2
                     1  6  7      +  3  6  8  8  0
                        7            1  1  1
              -      1  5  2         7  0  0  7  2
                        1  5  2
                           7
              -         1  5  2
                              0
```

- Let's check our work. How can we determine if our quotient has been calculated correctly?
  - *We can multiply the quotient and the divisor. If we calculated correctly, the product would be equal to the dividend.*
- What is $3,688 \times 19$?
  - *70,072; the product is equal to the dividend, so our calculations are correct.*

Example 2 (10 minutes)

Display the expression 14,175 ÷ 315.

- **What is different with this expression?**
  - *The divisor has three digits.*
- **How can we represent 315?**
  - *We can reference 315 as 315 ones.*
- **Let's first estimate the quotient. Look at the dividend. To what number could 14,175 be rounded?**
  - *Student response may vary but should represent an efficient number to compute the estimation (e.g., 15,000).*
- **Look at the divisor. To what number can 315 be rounded?**
  - *Student responses may vary but should reflect work done in Lesson 12 where students discovered estimates of quotients are most accurate the closer the dividend is to a multiple of 10 (e.g., 300).*
- **Let's divide 15,000 by 300.**

Display the following:

$$15,000 \div 300$$

- **Divide each number by one hundred for efficiency.**

Display the following:

$$15,000 \div 300$$
$$15,000 \div 100 \div 3$$
$$150 \div 3 = 50$$

Example 2

Divide 14,175 ÷ 315.

   a.   **Estimate:**

$$\mathbf{15,000 \div 300}$$
$$\mathbf{15,000 \div 100 \div 3}$$
$$\mathbf{150 \div 3 = 50}$$

- **Can we divide 1,417 tens into 315 groups or into groups of 315?**
  - *Yes*
- **Multiply the divisor by 50. What do you notice?**
  - $315 \times 50 = 15,750$; *our estimate is too large.*
- **Discuss with a partner what number should be multiplied to the divisor.**
  - *Answers may vary. Students should determine to multiply the divisor by 40.*
- **Record 4 in the tens place. This represents 4 tens.**

> **Scaffolding:**
>
> Students may benefit from making a table of multiples of 315 to reference.

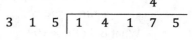

Lesson 13:   Dividing Multi-Digit Numbers Using the Algorithm

EUREKA MATH

- Multiply the divisor by 4 (tens) and record.
  - $315 \times 4 = 1,260$
- What does 1,260 represent?
  - 1,260 *tens*

- Record 1 in the ten thousands place, 2 in the thousands place, 6 in the hundreds place, and 0 in the tens place because we know 1,260 tens is the same as 12,600. Find the remainder in the tens place.
  - $1,417 - 1,260 = 157$
- Can we divide 157 tens by 315?
  - *We must regroup first.*
- We need to regroup 157 tens into 1,570 ones and combine with the 5 already in the ones place.
- How many times does 315 go into 1,575 ones?
  - $5 \times 315 = 1,575$; 5 *times*
- Record 5 in the ones place, and find the remainder in the ones place.
  - $1,575 - 1,575 = 0$

```
                      4   5
  3   1   5 | 1   4   1   7   5
                  2
          -   1   2   6   0
                  1   5   7   5
                          2
              -   1   5   7   5
                              0
```

---

b. Use the algorithm to divide 14,175 ÷ 315. Check your work.

```
                      4   5
  3   1   5 | 1   4   1   7   5
                  2
          -   1   2   6   0
                  1   5   7   5
                          2
              -   1   5   7   5
                              0
```

```
                          3   1   5
                      ×       4   5
                              2
                  1   5   7   5
                      2
            +   1   2   6   0   0
                  1
                  1   4   1   7   5
```

- Let's check our work. How can we determine if our quotient has been calculated correctly?
  - *We can multiply the quotient and the divisor. If we calculated correctly, the product would be equal to the dividend.*
- What is 45×315?
  - 14,175; *the product is equal to the dividend, so our calculations are correct.*

Exercises 1–5 (15 minutes)

Use estimation and divide using the algorithm. Students work individually or in pairs.

Lesson 13:   Dividing Multi-Digit Numbers Using the Algorithm   135

© 2015 Great Minds. eureka-math.org
G6-M2-TE-B2-1.3.1-01.2016

Exercises 1–5

For each exercise,

    a.   **Estimate.**

    b.   **Divide using the algorithm, explaining your work using place value.**

1. $484,692 \div 78$

    a.   **Estimate:** $480,000 \div 80 = 6,000$

    b.

```
              6   2   1   4
   7   8 | 4  8   4   6   9   2
           4
         - 4  6   8
           1  6   6
              1
            - 1  5   6
              1   0   9
                -   7   8
                    3   1   2
                    7   3
                  - 3   1   2
                        0
```

    484 *thousands* $\div$ 78: **6 *thousands***

    166 *hundreds* $\div$ 78: **2 *hundreds***

    109 *tens* $\div$ 78: **1 *ten***

    312 *ones* $\div$ 78: **4 *ones***

2. $281,886 \div 33$

    a.   **Estimate:** $270,000 \div 30 = 9,000$

    b.

```
              8   5   4   2
   3   3 | 2  8   1   8   8   6
           2
         - 2  6   4
           1  7   8
              1
            - 1  6   5
              1   3   8
                  1
                - 1   3   2
                      6   6
                    - 6   6
                        0
```

    281 *thousands* $\div$ 33: **8 *thousands***

    178 *hundreds* $\div$ 33: **5 *hundreds***

    138 *tens* $\div$ 33: **4 *tens***

    66 *ones* $\div$ 33: **2 *ones***

EUREKA
MATH

3. 2,295,517 ÷ 37

    a. **Estimate: 2,400,000 ÷ 40 = 60,000**

    b.

```
                        6   2   0   4   1
          3   7 |  2   2   9   5   5   1   7            229 ten thousands ÷ 37:  6 ten thousands
                        4
                -   2   2   2
                        7   5                           75 thousands ÷ 37:  2 thousands
                        1
                    -   7   4
                        1   5                           15 hundreds ÷ 37:  0 hundreds
                    -       0
                        1   5   1                        151 tens ÷ 37:  4 tens
                            2
                    -   1   4   8                        37 ones ÷ 37:  1 one
                                3   7
                            -   3   7
                                    0
```

4. 952,448 ÷ 112

    a. **Estimate: 1,000,000 ÷ 100 = 10,000**

    b.

```
                        8   5   0   4
      1   1   2 |  9   5   2   4   4   8                 952 thousands ÷ 112:  8 thousands
                        1
                -   8   9   6
                        5   6   4                        564 hundreds ÷ 112:  5 hundreds
                        1
                    -   5   6   0
                            4   4                         44 tens ÷ 112:  0 tens
                        -       0
                            4   4   8                     448 ones ÷ 112:  4 ones
                        -   4   4   8
                                    0
```

5. 1,823,535 ÷ 245

    a. Estimate: 1,800,000 ÷ 200 = 9,000

    b.

```
                              7   4   4   3
      2   4   5 | 1   8   2   3   5   3   5        1,823 thousands ÷ 245:  7 thousands
                      3   3
                  -   1   7   1   5                 1,085 hundreds ÷ 245:  4 hundreds
                      1   0   8   5
                          1   2
                      -   9   8   0                 1,053 tens ÷ 245:  4 tens
                      1   0   5   3
                          1   2
                      -   9   8   0                 735 ones ÷ 245:  3 ones
                          7   3   5
                              1
                      -   7   3   5
                              0
```

Closing (5 minutes)

▪ Explain in your own words how the division algorithm works.

    ▫ *Answers may vary. Sample response: The division algorithm shows successive estimates of the quotient organized by place value, or the division algorithm breaks one large division problem into several smaller ones organized by place value.*

Exit Ticket (5 minutes)

© 2015 Great Minds. eureka-math.org
G6-M2-TE-B2-1.3.1-01.2016

Name _____ Date _____

Lesson 13: Dividing Multi-Digit Numbers Using the Algorithm

Exit Ticket

Divide using the division algorithm: 392,196 ÷ 87.

Exit Ticket Sample Solutions

Divide using the division algorithm: 392,196 ÷ 87.

```
                      4   5   0   8
      8   7  │  3   9   2   1   9   6
                      2
              −   3   4   8
                      4   4   1
                          3
                  −   4   3   5
                          6   9
                      −       0
                          6   9   6
                              5
                      −   6   9   6
                                  0
```

Problem Set Sample Solutions

Divide using the division algorithm.

1. 1,634 ÷ 19
    86

2. 2,450 ÷ 25
    98

3. 22,274 ÷ 37
    602

4. 21,361 ÷ 41
    521

5. 34,874 ÷ 53
    658

6. 50,902 ÷ 62
    821

7. 70,434 ÷ 78
    903

8. 91,047 ÷ 89
    1,023

9. 115,785 ÷ 93
    1,245

10. 207,968 ÷ 97
    2,144

11. 7,735 ÷ 119
    65

12. 21,948 ÷ 354
    62

13. 72,372 ÷ 111
    652

14. 74,152 ÷ 124
    598

EUREKA
MATH

15. $182,727 \div 257$

711

16. $396,256 \div 488$

812

17. $730,730 \div 715$

1,022

18. $1,434,342 \div 923$

1,554

19. $1,775,296 \div 32$

55,478

20. $1,144,932 \div 12$

95,411

Lesson 14: The Division Algorithm—Converting Decimal Division into Whole Number Division Using Fractions

Student Outcomes

- Students use their knowledge of dividing multi-digit numbers to solve for quotients of multi-digit decimals.
- Students understand the mathematical concept of decimal placement in the divisor and the dividend and its connection to multiplying by powers of 10.

Classwork

Opening Exercise (5 minutes)

Opening Exercise

Divide $\frac{1}{2} \div \frac{1}{10}$. Use a tape diagram to support your reasoning.

This question is asking the following: $\frac{1}{2}$ is $\frac{1}{10}$ of what number?

?

$\frac{1}{2}$

1 unit → $\frac{1}{2}$

10 units → $10 \times \frac{1}{2} = 5$

Relate the model to the invert and multiply rule.

$\frac{1}{2} \div \frac{1}{10} = \frac{1}{2} \times \frac{10}{1} = \frac{10}{2} = 5$

EUREKA MATH

Example 1 (5 minutes)

- Let's look at the Opening Exercise another way. We can represent $\frac{1}{2} \div \frac{1}{10}$ using decimals.

- We can represent the fractions $\frac{1}{2}$ and $\frac{1}{10}$ with which decimals?

  - *One-half can be represented with 0.5, and one-tenth can be represented by 0.1.*

- Display the following:

$$\frac{1}{2} \div \frac{1}{10}$$
$$0.5 \div 0.1$$

- This expression can be represented with the same interpretation as the Opening Exercise: 5 tenths is 1 tenth of what number?

- Let's model this question with a tape diagram.

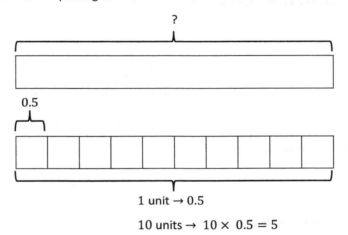

1 unit → 0.5

10 units → 10 × 0.5 = 5

- What do you notice about the diagram and the quotient?

  - *The diagram is set up exactly the same as in the Opening Exercise with the fraction, and the quotient is the same. Since $\frac{1}{2}$ is equivalent to 0.5, and $\frac{1}{10}$ is equivalent to 0.1, the quotients must be the same.*

- Look back at the problem: $0.5 \div 0.1$. Rewrite this division expression as a fraction.

  - $\frac{0.5}{0.1}$

- How can we express the divisor as a whole number?

  - *Multiply by a fraction equal to one.*

- Choose a fraction to multiply in order to express the divisor as a whole number.

  - *I could multiply $\frac{0.5}{0.1}$ by $\frac{10}{10}$ to represent the divisor as the whole number 1.*

Lesson 14: The Division Algorithm—Converting Decimal Division into Whole Number Division Using Fractions

143

- Find the product of $\frac{0.5}{0.1} \times \frac{10}{10}$.

  □ $\frac{0.5}{0.1} \times \frac{10}{10} = \frac{5}{1} = 5$

- What do you notice about the quotient?

  □ *It is the same as when we used a tape diagram to determine the quotient.*

- Why do you think the quotients are the same?

  □ *They are the same because I multiplied the divisor and the dividend by the same power of ten.*

- What conjecture can you make?

  □ *Because the divisor and the dividend both became ten times greater, when we write the numbers as ten times as much, we move the decimal to the right one place.*

Example 1

Evaluate the expression. Use a tape diagram to support your answer.

$0.5 \div 0.1$

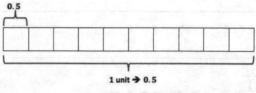

1 unit → 0.5

10 units → 10×0.5 = 5

Rewrite $0.5 \div 0.1$ as a fraction.

$\frac{0.5}{0.1}$

Express the divisor as a whole number.

$\frac{0.5}{0.1} \times \frac{10}{10} = \frac{5}{1} = 5$

Exercises 1–3 (5 minutes)

Students can work on the exercises alone or in pairs. Students convert the decimal division expressions to fractional division questions in order to create a whole number divisor.

Exercises 1–3

Convert the decimal division expressions to fractional division expressions in order to create whole number divisors. You do not need to find the quotients. Explain the movement of the decimal point. The first exercise has been completed for you.

1. **$18.6 \div 2.3$**

    $\frac{18.6}{2.3} \times \frac{10}{10} = \frac{186}{23}$

    $186 \div 23$

    I multiplied both the dividend and the divisor by ten, or by one power of ten, so each decimal point moved one place to the right because they grew larger by ten.

Lesson 14: The Division Algorithm—Converting Decimal Division into Whole
Number Division Using Fractions

EUREKA MATH

2. $14.04 \div 4.68$

$$\frac{14.04}{4.86} \times \frac{100}{100} = \frac{1404}{486}$$

$1,404 \div 486$

I multiplied both the dividend and divisor by one hundred, or by two powers of ten, so each decimal point moved two places to the right because they grew larger by two powers of ten.

3. $0.162 \div 0.036$

$$\frac{0.162}{0.036} \times \frac{1,000}{1,000} = \frac{162}{36}$$

$162 \div 36$

I multiplied both the dividend and divisor by one thousand, or three powers of ten, so each decimal point moved three places to the right because they grew larger by three powers of ten.

Example 2 (5 minutes)

- We determined that when we multiply a divisor by a power of ten, the decimal point is moved to the right the number of times we multiply by a power of ten. How many places does the decimal point move to the right when we multiply the divisor by ten?
    - *It moves one place to the right.*
- Explain why the decimal point moves twice to the right when we multiply the divisor by one hundred?
    - *It moves two places to the right because we have multiplied by a power of ten twice.*
- We can use decomposition to explain.

Display the expression $25.2 \div 0.72$.

- We can express the divisor as a whole number by multiplying it by one hundred.

Display the expression 0.72×100.

- Because we can decompose 100 into 10×10, we can also express the expression as $0.72 \times 10 \times 10$.
- Multiply 0.72×10.
    - 7.2
- What do you notice about the product?
    - *It is ten times greater than the original.*
- Multiply 7.2×10.
    - 72
- What movement did the decimal point make in this process?
    - *It moved two places to the right.*
- What do you notice about the product?
    - *It is ten times greater than the last step and one hundred times greater than the original.*
- How many times does the decimal point move to the right when we multiply a number by 1,000?
    - *It will move to the right three places because* $1,000 = 10 \times 10 \times 10$.

- Let's use this information to divide $25.2 \div 0.72$. Express this as a fraction.

  □ $\dfrac{25.2}{0.72}$

- Now you can easily choose a fraction to multiply in order to express the divisor as a whole number.

  □ $\dfrac{25.2}{0.72} \times \dfrac{100}{100} = \dfrac{2,520}{72}$

- Use the division algorithm to find the quotient.

  □ $\dfrac{2,520}{72} = 35$

Example 2

Evaluate the expression. First, convert the decimal division expression to a fractional division expression in order to create a whole number divisor.

$25.2 \div 0.72$

$\dfrac{25.2}{0.72} \times \dfrac{100}{100} = \dfrac{2,520}{72}$

```
                3   5
      ┌──────────────
 7  2 │ 2   5   2   0
      │ 2   1   6
      │ ───────
      │     3   6   0
      │         1
      │     3   6   0
      │     ───────
      │             0
```

Use the division algorithm to find the quotient.

$25.2 \div 0.72 = 35$

- Using a calculator, multiply to check that the quotient is accurate.

  □ $35 \times 0.72 = 25.2$

Exercises 4–7 (10 minutes)

Students work on the exercises individually or in partners. Students convert the decimal division expressions to fractional division questions in order to create a whole number divisor. Quotients are computed using the division algorithm. Students are encouraged to check their work with a calculator.

Lesson 14:   The Division Algorithm—Converting Decimal Division into Whole
Number Division Using Fractions

EUREKA
MATH

Exercises 4–7

Convert the decimal division expressions to fractional division expressions in order to create whole number divisors. Compute the quotients using the division algorithm. Check your work with a calculator.

4. $2,000 \div 3.2$

$$\frac{2,000}{3.2} \times \frac{10}{10} = \frac{20,000}{32}$$

```
                    6   2   5
        3   2 │ 2   0   0   0
            −   1   9   2
                        8   0
                    −   6   4
                        1   6   0
                    −   1   6   0
                                0
```

$$20,000 \div 32 = 625$$
$$625 \times 32 = 20,000$$
$$2,000 \div 3.2 = 625$$
$$625 \times 3.2 = 2,000$$

5. $3,581.9 \div 4.9$

$$\frac{3,581.9}{4.9} \times \frac{10}{10} = \frac{35,819}{49}$$

```
                    7   3   1
        4   9 │ 3   5   8   1   9
                    6
            −   3   4   3
                    1   5   1
                        2
                −   1   4   7
                            4   9
                        −   4   9
                                0
```

$$35,819 \div 49 = 731$$
$$731 \times 49 = 35,819$$
$$3,581.9 \div 4.9 = 731$$
$$731 \times 4.9 = 3,581.9$$

6. $893.76 \div 0.21$

$$\frac{893.76}{0.21} \times \frac{100}{100} = \frac{89,376}{21}$$

```
                4   2   5   6
    2   1 | 8   9   3   7   6
        -   8   4
                5   3
            -   4   2
                1   1   7
            -   1   0   5
                    1   2   6
                -   1   2   6
                            0
```

$$89,376 \div 21 = 4,256$$
$$4,256 \times 21 = 89,376$$
$$893.76 \div 0.21 = 4,256$$
$$4,256 \times 0.21 = 893.76$$

7. $6.194 \div 0.326$

$$\frac{6.194}{0.326} \times \frac{1,000}{1,000} = \frac{6,194}{326}$$

```
                    1   9
    3   2   6 | 6   1   9   4
            -   3   2   6
                2   9   3   4
                    2   5
            -   2   9   3   4
                            0
```

$$6,194 \div 326 = 19$$
$$19 \times 326 = 6,194$$
$$6.194 \div 0.326 = 19$$
$$19 \times 0.326 = 6.194$$

Example 3 (5 minutes)

This example is to provide students a real-world context for division of decimals. Students recall information from Module 1 and apply unit rate.

- What is this question asking us to find?
  - *This question is asking me to find the unit rate. I need to divide the number of miles by the number of hours so that I can determine the number of miles the plane flew in 1 hour, as we did in Module 1.*

Lesson 14:   The Division Algorithm—Converting Decimal Division into Whole
             Number Division Using Fractions

© 2015 Great Minds. eureka-math.org
G6-M2-TE-B2-1.3.1-01.2016

- Rewrite the expression $3{,}625.26 \div 6.9$ as a fraction.

    □ $\dfrac{3{,}625.26}{6.9}$

- How can we express the divisor as a whole number?

    □ *Multiply by a fraction equal to one.*

- Choose a fraction to multiply in order to express the divisor as a whole number.

    □ *I could multiply $\dfrac{3{,}625.26}{6.9}$ by $\dfrac{10}{10}$ to represent the divisor as the whole number* 1.

- Find the product of $\dfrac{3{,}625.26}{6.9} \times \dfrac{10}{10}$.

    □ $\dfrac{3{,}6252.6}{69}$

- Show how we can rewrite $3{,}625.26$ (362,526 hundredths) and 6.9 (69 tenths) using the same units.

    □ $36{,}252.6$ *tenths* $\div$ 69 *tenths.*

- Notice that the decimal in both the dividend and the divisor shifted one place to the right. This resulted in a whole number divisor. Now we can evaluate by dividing $36{,}252.6 \div 69$ using the division algorithm.

Example 3

A plane travels 3,625.26 miles in 6.9 hours. What is the plane's unit rate?

Represent this situation with a fraction.

$\dfrac{3{,}625.26}{6.9}$

Represent this situation using the same units.

$36{,}252.6$ *tenths* $\div$ **69** *tenths*

Estimate the quotient.

$35{,}000 \div 70 = 500$

Express the divisor as a whole number.

$\dfrac{3{,}625.26}{6.9} \times \dfrac{10}{10} = \dfrac{36{,}252.6}{69}$

Use the division algorithm to find the quotient.

$$
\begin{array}{r}
5\ \ 2\ \ 5.\ \ 4 \\
6\ \ 9\ \big|\ 3\ \ 6\ \ 2\ \ 5\ \ 2.\ \ 6 \\
4 \\
-\ 3\ \ 4\ \ 5 \\
\hline
1\ \ 7\ \ 5 \\
7 \\
-\ 1\ \ 3\ \ 8 \\
\hline
3\ \ 7\ \ 2 \\
4 \\
-\ 3\ \ 4\ \ 5 \\
\hline
2\ \ 7\ \ 6 \\
3 \\
-\ 2\ \ 7\ \ 6 \\
\hline
0
\end{array}
$$

Use multiplication to check your work.

$525.4 \times 69 = 36,252.6$

- Let's check our answer to ensure that it is reasonable. What are some different ways that we can do this?
  - *We can multiply the quotient with the original divisor and see if we get the original dividend.*
    $6.9 \times 525.4 = 3,625.26.$
  - *We could also compare the quotient to estimate to check our answer. $3,500 \div 7 = 500$. Because we rounded down, we should expect our estimate to be a little less than the actual answer, 525.4.*

Closing (5 minutes)

- Explain a strategy to convert a decimal divisor into a whole number divisor.
  - *In order to convert a decimal divisor into a whole number divisor, we could multiply by powers of ten. We continue to multiply by a power of ten until the decimal divisor is a whole number divisor. We must also multiply the dividend by the same power of ten for equality.*
- Must we always multiply a decimal divisor by a power of ten to convert it to a whole number divisor?
  - *Answers may vary. Allow students to project inferences.*

Present the following problem: $105 \div 3.5$.

- What could I multiply the divisor by to convert it to a whole number divisor?
  - *Answers may vary. Elicit responses, where some students may suggest multiplying by ten, as they have practiced in this lesson.*
- Is there a more efficient means of converting the decimal divisor into a whole number divisor?
  - *Answers may vary. Elicit responses, where some students may suggest multiplying the divisor and dividend by 2.*

Lesson 14:   The Division Algorithm—Converting Decimal Division into Whole
              Number Division Using Fractions

© 2015 Great Minds. eureka-math.org
G6-M2-TE-B2-1.3.1-01.2016

- If we multiplied the divisor by 2, that would convert the decimal to the whole number, 7. Since we multiplied the divisor by 2, we must also multiply the dividend by 2, which is 210. What do you find convenient with this strategy?
  - *Answers may vary. Responses should include that using mental math helped create a less complex problem in comparison to multiplying by powers of ten.*

Preview that the next lesson practices using mental math strategies to efficiently divide whole numbers and decimals.

Exit Ticket (5 minutes)

© 2015 Great Minds. eureka-math.org
G6-M2-TE-B2-1.3.1-01.2016

Lesson 14: The Division Algorithm—Converting Decimal Division into Whole Number Division Using Fractions

Name _____   Date _____

Exit Ticket

Estimate quotients. Convert decimal division expressions to fractional division expressions to create whole number divisors. Compute the quotient using the division algorithm. Check your work with a calculator and your estimate.

1.   Lisa purchased almonds for $3.50 per pound. She spent a total of $24.50. How many pounds of almonds did she purchase?

2.   Divide: $125.01 \div 5.4$.

© 2015 Great Minds. eureka-math.org
G6-M2-TE-B2-1.3.1-01.2016

Exit Ticket Sample Solutions

Estimate quotients. Convert decimal division expressions to fractional division expressions to create whole number divisor. Compute the quotient using the division algorithm. Check your work with a calculator and your estimate.

1. **Lisa purchased almonds for $3.50 per pound. She spent a total of $24.50. How many pounds of almonds did she purchase?**

$$\frac{24.50}{3.50} \times \frac{100}{100} = \frac{245}{35}$$

Estimate: $270 \div 30 = 9$

```
                    7
    3   5  | 2   4   5
                3
        -   2   4   5
                    0
```

Lisa purchased 7 *pounds of almonds. This is close to my estimate of* 9.

$7 \times 35 = 245$

$7 \times 3.5 = 24.5$

2. **Divide:** $125.01 \div 5.4$.

$$\frac{125.01}{5.4} \times \frac{10}{10} = \frac{1250.1}{54}$$

Estimate: $125 \div 5 = 25$

```
                2   3.   1   5
    5   4  | 1   2   5   0.  1   0
        -   1   0   8
                1   7   0
                    1
            -   1   6   2
                    8   1
                -   5   4
                    2   7   0
                        2
                -   2   7   6
                        0
```

The quotient of 125.01 *and* 5.4 *is* 23.15. *This is close to my estimate of* 25.

$23.15 \times 54 = 1250.1$

$23.15 \times 5.4 = 125.01$

Problem Set Sample Solutions

Convert decimal division expressions to fractional division expressions to create whole number divisors.

1. $35.7 \div 0.07$

$$\frac{35.7}{0.07} \times \frac{100}{100} = \frac{3{,}570}{7}$$

2. $486.12 \div 0.6$

$$\frac{486.12}{0.6} \times \frac{10}{10} = \frac{4{,}861.2}{6}$$

3. $3.43 \div 0.035$

$$\frac{3.43}{0.035} \times \frac{1{,}000}{1{,}000} = \frac{3{,}430}{35}$$

4. $5418.54 \div 0.009$

$$\frac{5{,}418.54}{0.009} \times \frac{1{,}000}{1{,}000} = \frac{5{,}418{,}540}{9}$$

5. $812.5 \div 1.25$

$$\frac{812.5}{1.25} \times \frac{100}{100} = \frac{81{,}250}{125}$$

6. $17.343 \div 36.9$

$$\frac{17.343}{36.9} \times \frac{10}{10} = \frac{173.43}{369}$$

Estimate quotients. Convert decimal division expressions to fractional division expressions to create whole number divisors. Compute the quotients using the division algorithm. Check your work with a calculator and your estimates.

7. Norman purchased 3.5 lb. of his favorite mixture of dried fruits to use in a trail mix. The total cost was $16.87. How much does the fruit cost per pound?

$$\frac{16.87}{3.5} \times \frac{10}{10} = \frac{168.7}{35}$$

Estimate: $16 \div 4 = 4$

The dried fruit costs $4.82 *per pound. This is close to my estimate of* 4.

8. Divide: $994.14 \div 18.9$

$$\frac{994.14}{18.9} \times \frac{10}{10} = \frac{9{,}941.4}{189}$$

Estimate: $100 \div 2 = 50$

The quotient is 52.6. *This is close to my estimate of* 50.

EUREKA
MATH

9. Daryl spent $4.68 on each pound of trail mix. He spent a total of $14.04. How many pounds of trail mix did he purchase?

$$\frac{14.04}{4.68} \times \frac{100}{100} = \frac{1,404}{468}$$

Estimate: $15 \div 5 = 3$

Daryl purchased 3 *pounds of trail mix. This is my estimate.*

10. Mamie saved $161.25. This is 25% of the amount she needs to save. How much money does Mamie need to save?

$$\frac{161.25}{0.25} \times \frac{100}{100} = \frac{16,125}{25}$$

Estimate: $1,600 \div 2 = 800$

Mamie needs to save $645. *This is close to my estimate of* 800.

11. Kareem purchased several packs of gum to place in gift baskets for $1.26 each. He spent a total of $8.82. How many packs of gum did he buy?

$$\frac{8.82}{1.26} \times \frac{100}{100} = \frac{882}{126}$$

Estimate: $9 \div 1 = 9$

Kareem bought 7 *packs of gum. This is close to my estimate of* 9.

12. Jerod is making candles from beeswax. He has 132.72 ounces of beeswax. If each candle uses 8.4 ounces of beeswax, how many candles can he make? Will there be any wax left over?

$$\frac{132.72}{8.4} \times \frac{10}{10} = \frac{1,327.2}{84}$$

Estimate: $120 \div 8 = 15$

The quotient is 15.8. *This means that Jerod can make* 15 *candles. This is close to my estimate. There will be wax left over.*

13. There are 20.5 cups of batter in the bowl. This represents 0.4 of the entire amount of batter needed for a recipe. How many cups of batter are needed?

$$\frac{20.5}{0.4} \times \frac{10}{10} = \frac{205}{4}$$

Estimate: $200 \div 4 = 50$

The number of cups of batter needed for the recipe is 51.25. *This is close to my estimate.*

14. Divide: $159.12 \div 6.8$

$$\frac{159.12}{6.8} \times \frac{10}{10} = \frac{1,591.2}{68}$$

Estimate: $160 \div 8 = 20$

The quotient is 23.4. *This is close to my estimate.*

15. Divide: $167.67 \div 8.1$

$$\frac{167.67}{8.1} \times \frac{10}{10} = \frac{1,676.7}{81}$$

Estimate: $160 \div 8 = 20$

The quotient is 20.7. *This is close to my estimate.*

Lesson 15: The Division Algorithm—Converting Decimal Division into Whole Number Division Using Mental Math

Student Outcomes

- Students use mental math and their knowledge of dividing multi-digit numbers to solve for quotients of multi-digit decimals.
- Students understand the mathematical concept of decimal placement in the divisor and the dividend and its connection to multiplying by powers of 10.

Lesson Notes

Students have utilized mental math techniques in previous grade levels. Mental math techniques aid in efficient computation and application of number sense. In this lesson, students utilize mental math techniques that include compensation, where students convert problems to easier ones with the same answer. They also divide by 5 efficiently by dividing by 10 and doubling. Students efficiently divide by 4 by halving twice, which leads into the strategy to efficiently divide by 8, which is halving three times. Mental math is computation that is thought, but on classwork, students are asked to write down their thoughts. These methods are easier than they look in written form. The idea is to have students apply the techniques and practice them, not memorize them.

Classwork

Opening Exercise (3 minutes)

Opening Exercise

Use mental math to evaluate the numeric expressions.

a. $99 + 44$

   44 *gives* 1 *to* 99.

   $100 + 43 = 143$

b. $86 - 39$

   ***Increase both by* 1.**

   $87 - 40 = 47$

c. 50×14

   ***Double* 50; *halve* 14.**

   $100 \times 7 = 700$

Lesson 15:   The Division Algorithm—Converting Decimal Division into Whole
                              Number Division Using Mental Math

> d. $180 \div 5$
>
> *Double both.*
>
> $360 \div 10 = 36$

Example 1 (8 minutes): Use Mental Math to Find Quotients

- We have been working with the division algorithm and have applied the algorithm to division of decimals. Let's see if there is a way to make our computations more efficient.

Display the expression: $105 \div 35$

- In the past lesson, we utilized the powers of ten to help us estimate and find quotients. Discuss with your partner if it would be efficient to use a power of ten to estimate or to evaluate this expression.

  - *Student responses may vary. Students should determine that raising either the dividend or the divisor by a power of ten does not make the expression easier to evaluate.*

- Is 10 the only number we can utilize in this strategy? Can we multiply or divide both the dividend and the divisor by any same number and reach the same quotient? Let's demonstrate a simpler problem.

Display the expression: $25 \div 5$

Although this is a basic fact, it provides reasoning for the mental math technique.

- We can interpret this problem as follows: How many fives are in twenty-five?

Create and display the following tape diagram:

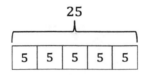

- There are 5 fives in 25. What if each of the units of five was doubled? What number is represented by 5 tens?

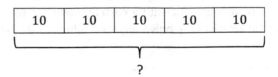

  - *5 tens is* 50.

Display the corresponding division expressions:

$$25 \div 5 = 5$$
$$50 \div 10 = 5$$

- What do you notice about the dividends and the divisors?

  - *We multiplied both the original dividend and divisor by* 2.

- What do you notice about the quotients?

  - *They are the same.*

- What conjuncture can you make about multiplying both the dividend and the divisor by 2?
  - *Multiplying both the dividend and the divisor by the same number does not change the quotient.*

Display the expression: $105 \div 35$, again.

- With your partner, multiply both the dividend and the divisor by 2. What is the resulting expression?
  - *The resulting expression is $210 \div 70$.*

- What do you notice about the dividend and the divisor now? Discuss with your partner.
  - *Student responses may vary. Students should determine that by multiplying both the dividend and the divisor by 2, the resulting expression can be easily computed using one-digit arithmetic facts.*

- Evaluate $210 \div 70$.
  - $$\frac{210 \div 10}{70 \div 10} = \frac{21}{7} = 3$$

Evaluate $105 \div 35$ with a calculator, and display to the class.

- What do you notice about the quotients?
  - *They are the same.*

> **Scaffolding:**
>
> Students may benefit from seeing this problem represented with a tape diagram. When creating the diagram, be mindful that, regardless of how the original units are drawn, the doubled units are exactly twice the size of the original units. This could take up a lot of space, so be mindful of how the original units are drawn.

Example 1: Use Mental Math to Find Quotients

Use mental math to evaluate $105 \div 35$.

$$\frac{105 \times 2}{35 \times 2} = \frac{210}{70} = \frac{21}{7} = 3$$

Exercises 1–4 (5 minutes)

In these exercises, students practice mental math techniques with a partner. Students are encouraged to detail individual techniques with their partner and compare the quotients when finished. Students are also encouraged to compare strategies and determine which are most efficient for each problem. Circulate the room, and monitor conversations. Student responses for the exercises are only suggested solutions. Any response that leads to efficiency and accuracy is acceptable.

Exercises 1–4

Use mental math techniques to evaluate the expressions.

1. $770 \div 14$

   $$\frac{770 \div 7}{14 \div 7} = \frac{110}{2} = 55$$

2. $1,005 \div 5$

   $$\frac{1,005 \times 2}{5 \times 2} = \frac{2,010}{10} = 201$$

Lesson 15:   The Division Algorithm—Converting Decimal Division into Whole Number Division Using Mental Math

3. $1{,}500 \div 8$

$$\frac{1{,}500 \div 2}{8 \div 2} = \frac{750 \div 2}{4 \div 2} = \frac{375}{2} = 187.5$$

4. $1{,}260 \div 5$

$$\frac{1{,}250}{10} = 126 \times 2 = 252$$

Example 2 (3 minutes): Mental Math and Division of Decimals

In Example 2, students apply mental math strategies to division of decimals.

Display on the board: $175 \div 3.5$

- What can we do to make this expression easier to evaluate?
    - *Student responses may vary. Students should see that multiplying the divisor by 2 creates a whole number that easily divides into the dividend that has been doubled.*
- Multiply both the divisor and the dividend by 2. What is the resulting expression?
    - $350 \div 7$
- Now we have an expression that can be evaluated using one-digit arithmetic facts. Evaluate the expression.
    - $350 \div 7 = 50$
- Could we have multiplied both the divisor and the dividend by a power of ten?
    - *We could have multiplied by 10 to create a whole number divisor, but it would not be more efficient.*

Example 2: Mental Math and Division of Decimals

Evaluate the expression $175 \div 3.5$ using mental math techniques.

$$\frac{175 \times 2}{3.5 \times 2} = \frac{350}{7} = 50$$

Exercises 5–7 (4 minutes)

Exercises 5–7

Use mental math techniques to evaluate the expressions.

5. $25 \div 6.25$

$$\frac{25 \times 4}{6.25 \times 4} = \frac{100}{25} = 4$$

6. $6.3 \div 1.5$

$$\frac{6.3 \times 2}{1.5 \times 2} = \frac{12.6}{3} = 4.2$$

7. $425 \div 2.5$

$$\frac{425 \times 2}{2.5 \times 2} = \frac{850}{5} = 170$$

Example 3 (5 minutes): Mental Math and the Division Algorithm

Students extend mental math techniques to division of decimals that may require the use of the algorithm.

Display the expression: $4,564 \div 3.5$

- ▪ What is a good strategy to use to evaluate this expression efficiently?
    - ▫ *Multiply both the dividend and the divisor by 2. That produces a whole number divisor.*
- ▪ Multiply both the dividend and the divisor by 2. What is the expression?
    - ▫ $9,128 \div 7$
- ▪ I think our mental math has gotten us as far as we can take it, other than estimation. What can we utilize to find the quotient?
    - ▫ *The division algorithm*
- ▪ Work with a partner, and evaluate the expression.

Example 3: Mental Math and the Division Algorithm

Evaluate the expression $4,564 \div 3.5$ using mental math techniques and the division algorithm.

$$\frac{4,564 \times 2}{3.5 \times 2} = \frac{9,128}{7}$$

```
            1  3  0  4
     7 | 9  1  2  8
       -  7
          2  1
       -  2  1
             0  2
          -     0
                2  8
             -  2  8
                   0
```

Example 4 (7 minutes): Mental Math and Reasonable Work

This example is to provide students the opportunity to utilize mental math to check for reasonableness in a solution. This is envisioned to be a whole group discussion, where students can later practice solving these types of problems in the Problem Set.

Allow students to collaborate with their peers to determine where the decimal point should be placed, without calculation.

- ▫ *Answers may vary. Students should conclude through estimation that $54 \div 6 = 9$. Nine is in the ones place. Therefore, the decimal point should be placed after the 8 in the quotient.*

Lesson 15:   The Division Algorithm—Converting Decimal Division into Whole
                                  Number Division Using Mental Math

Allow students to use the division algorithm to find the quotient.

Example 4: Mental Math and Reasonable Work

Shelly was given this number sentence and was asked to place the decimal point correctly in the quotient.

$$55.6875 \div 6.75 = 0.825$$

Do you agree with Shelly?

No, I do not agree with Shelly. When I round the dividend to 54 and the divisor to 6, the quotient is 9. I know that 9 is in the ones place, so the decimal should be placed after the 8 in the quotient.

Divide to prove your answer is correct.

```
                      8.  2   5
  6   7   5 | 5   5   6   8.  7   5
              3   4
          -   5   4   0   0
              1   6   8   7
                  1   1
          -   1   3   5   0
              3   3   7   5
                  3   2
          -   3   3   7   5
                              0
```

Closing (5 minutes)

- What are the benefits of using mental math techniques when dividing? Talk with your partner. Share.
    - *Answers may vary, but students should conclude that mental math techniques aid in the efficiency of solving problems. Using mental math aids in choosing a course of action when dividing. Because of mental math techniques, we can use number sense to choose any strategy to divide.*
- Which mental math techniques work best for you? Talk with your partner. Share.
    - *Answers may vary, but students should describe situations where specific mental math strategies work best for them. Students should defend their stances while allowing others to disagree and explain their preferences.*

Exit Ticket (5 minutes)

Name _____ Date _____

Lesson 15: The Division Algorithm—Converting Decimal Division into Whole Number Division Using Mental Math

Exit Ticket

Evaluate the expression using mental math techniques and the division algorithm. Explain your reasoning.

$$18.75 \div 2.5$$

© 2015 Great Minds. eureka-math.org
G6-M2-TE-B2-1.3.1-01.2016

Exit Ticket Sample Solutions

Evaluate the expression using mental math techniques and the division algorithm. Explain your reasoning.

$$18.75 \div 2.5$$

$$\frac{18.75 \times 2}{2.5 \times 2} = \frac{37.5}{5}$$

I find it easier to divide by 5, so I doubled both the divisor and the dividend. I knew that the dividend would be divisible by 5 since it has a 5 in the hundredths place.

```
           7.  5
   5 | 3   7.  5
     -  3  5
           2   5
         -  2   5
                0
```

$18.75 \div 2.5 = 7.5$

Problem Set Sample Solutions

Use mental math, estimation, and the division algorithm to evaluate the expressions.

1. $118.4 \div 6.4$

   18.5

2. $314.944 \div 3.7$

   85.12

3. $1,840.5072 \div 23.56$

   78.12

4. $325 \div 2.5$

   130

5. $196 \div 3.5$

   56

6. $405 \div 4.5$

   90

7. $3,437.5 \div 5.5$

   625

8. $393.75 \div 5.25$

   75

9. $2,625 \div 6.25$

   420

10. $231 \div 8.25$

    28

11. $92 \div 5.75$

    16

12. $196 \div 12.25$

    16

13. $117 \div 6.5$

    18

14. $936 \div 9.75$

    96

15. $305 \div 12.2$

    25

Place the decimal point in the correct place to make the number sentence true.

16. $83.375 \div 2.3 = 3,625$

    $83.375 \div 2.3 = 36.25$

17. $183.575 \div 5,245 = 3.5$

    $183.575 \div 52.45 = 3.5$

18. $326,025 \div 9.45 = 3.45$

    $32.6025 \div 9.45 = 3.45$

19. $449.5 \div 725 = 6.2$

    $449.5 \div 72.5 = 6.2$

20. $446,642 \div 85.4 = 52.3$

    $4,466.42 \div 85.4 = 52.3$

6
GRADE

Mathematics Curriculum

Topic D

Number Theory—Thinking Logically About Multiplicative Arithmetic

6.NS.B.4

Focus Standard:	6.NS.B.4	Find the greatest common factor of two whole numbers less than or equal to 100 and the least common multiple of two whole numbers less than or equal to 12. Use the distributive property to express a sum of two whole numbers 1–100 with a common factor as a multiple of a sum of two whole numbers with no common factor. *For example, express* $36 + 8$ *as* $4(9 + 2)$.
Instructional Days:	4	
	Lesson 16:	Even and Odd Numbers (S)[1]
	Lesson 17:	Divisibility Tests for 3 and 9 (S)
	Lesson 18:	Least Common Multiple and Greatest Common Factor (P)
	Lesson 19:	The Euclidean Algorithm as an Application of the Long Division Algorithm (P)

Students have previously developed facility with multiplication and division. They now begin to reason logically about them in Topic D. Students apply odd and even number properties and divisibility rules to find factors and multiples. They extend this application to consider common factors and multiples and to find greatest common factors and least common multiples. Students explore and discover that Euclid's algorithm is a more efficient means of finding the greatest common factor of larger numbers, and they determine that Euclid's algorithm is based on long division.

---

[1]Lesson Structure Key: **P**-Problem Set Lesson, **M**-Modeling Cycle Lesson, **E**-Exploration Lesson, **S**-Socratic Lesson

Lesson 16: Even and Odd Numbers

Student Outcomes

▪ Students generalize rules for adding and multiplying even and odd numbers.

Lesson Notes

Students need poster paper and markers to complete the exercises.

Classwork

Discussion (15 minutes)

Present each question, and then allow students to share their thinking. Also, have students record notes in their student materials.

Opening Exercise

    a. **What is an even number?**

    Possible student responses:

- *An integer that can be evenly divided by 2*
- *A number whose unit digit is 0, 2, 4, 6, or 8*
- *All the multiples of 2*

    b. **List some examples of even numbers.**

    Answers will vary.

    c. **What is an odd number?**

    Possible student responses:

- *An integer that CANNOT be evenly divided by 2*
- *A number whose unit digit is 1, 3, 5, 7, or 9*
- *All the numbers that are NOT multiples of 2*

    d. **List some examples of odd numbers.**

    Answers will vary.

Present each question, and then discuss the answer using models.

What happens when we add two even numbers? Do we always get an even number?

Before holding a discussion about the process to answer the following questions, have students write or share their predictions.

Exercises 1–3

> ### Exercises 1–3
>
> 1. Why is the sum of two even numbers even?
>
>   a. Think of the problem $12 + 14$. Draw dots to represent each number.
>
>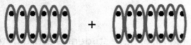
>
>   b. Circle pairs of dots to determine if any of the dots are left over.
>
>   *There are no dots leftover; the answer is even.*
>
>   c. Is this true every time two even numbers are added together? Why or why not?
>
>   *Since 12 is represented by 6 sets of two dots, and 14 is represented by 7 sets of two dots, the sum is 13 sets of two dots. This is true every time two even numbers are added together because even numbers never have dots left over when we are circling pairs. Therefore, the answer is always even.*

Before holding a discussion about the process to answer the following questions, have students write or share their predictions.

- Now, decide what happens when we add two odd numbers.

> 2. Why is the sum of two odd numbers even?
>
>   a. Think of the problem $11 + 15$. Draw dots to represent each number.
>
>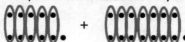
>
>   b. Circle pairs of dots to determine if any of the dots are left over.
>
>   *When we circle groups of two dots, there is one dot remaining in each representation because each addend is an odd number. When we look at the sum, however, the two remaining dots can form a pair, leaving us with a sum that is represented by groups of two dots. The sum is, therefore, even. Since each addend is odd, there is one dot for each addend that does not have a pair. However, these two dots can be paired together, which means there are no dots without a pair, making the sum an even number.*

Lesson 16:   Even and Odd Numbers

c.   **Is this true every time two odd numbers are added together? Why or why not?**

This is true every time two odd numbers are added together because every odd number has one dot remaining when we circle pairs of dots. Since each number has one dot remaining, these dots can be combined to make another pair. Therefore, no dots remain, resulting in an even sum.

▪ Use the same method we used in the two prior examples to show that the sum of an odd number and an even number is odd. Use the problem $14 + 11$.

3.   **Why is the sum of an even number and an odd number odd?**

a.   **Think of the problem $14 + 11$. Draw dots to represent each number.**

b.   **Circle pairs of dots to determine if any of the dots are left over.**

Students draw dots to represent each number. After circling pairs of dots, there is one dot left for the number 11, and the number 14 has no dots remaining. Since there is one dot left over, the sum is odd because not every dot has a pair.

MP.3 & MP.8

c.   **Is this true every time an even number and an odd number are added together? Why or why not?**

This is always true when an even number and an odd number are added together because only the odd number will have a dot remaining after we circle pairs of dots. Since this dot does not have a pair, the sum is odd.

d.   **What if the first addend is odd and the second is even? Is the sum still odd? Why or why not? For example, if we had $11 + 14$, would the sum be odd?**

The sum is still odd for two reasons. First, the commutative property states that changing the order of an addition problem does not change the answer. Because an even number plus an odd number is odd, then an odd number plus an even number is also odd. Second, it does not matter which addend is odd; there is still one dot remaining, making the sum odd.

Encourage struggling students to draw dots to prove their answer. It may also help to remind students of the commutative property to help them prove their answer.

Sum up the discussion by having students record notes in their handbooks.

Let's sum it up:

▪ *"Even" + "even" = "even"*

▪ *"Odd" + "odd" = "even"*

▪ *"Odd" + "even" = "odd"*

> *Scaffolding:*
>
> The teacher could also ask students if the same rules apply to subtraction. Using the same method for addition, have students determine if the rules apply to subtraction.

> *Scaffolding:*
>
> ▪ If students are struggling with the proofs, the teacher can present each proof as students take notes in their handbooks. Or, allow students time to explore, and have a few groups who did not struggle present at the end.
>
> ▪ Ask early finishers if the same rule applies to division.

Exploratory Challenge/Exercises 4–6 (20 minutes: 12 minutes for group work; 8 minutes for gallery walk and discussion)

Divide students into small groups. On poster paper, each group is asked to determine whether one of the following products is odd or even: the product of two even numbers, the product of two odd numbers, or the product of an even number and an odd number. Encourage students to use previous knowledge about even and odd numbers, the connection between addition and multiplication, and visual methods (e.g., dots) in their proofs.

Exploratory Challenge/Exercises 4–6

4. The product of two even numbers is even.

    Answers will vary, but one example answer is provided.

    Using the problem 6×14, students know that this is equivalent to six groups of fourteen, or $14 + 14 + 14 + 14 + 14 + 14$. Students also know that the sum of two even numbers is even; therefore, when adding the addends two at a time, the sum is always even. This means the sum of six even numbers is even, making the product even since it is equivalent to the sum.

    Using the problem 6×14, students can use the dots from previous examples.

    ```
    •••••••      •••••••      •••••••      •••••••      •••••••      •••••••
           +            +            +            +            +
    •••••••      •••••••      •••••••      •••••••      •••••••      •••••••
    ```

    From here, students can circle dots and see that there are no dots remaining, so the answer must be even.

5. The product of two odd numbers is odd.

    Answers will vary, but an example answer is provided.

    Using the problem 5×15, students know that this is equivalent to five groups of fifteen, or $15 + 15 + 15 + 15 + 15$. Students also know that the sum of two odd numbers is even, and the sum of an odd and even number is odd. When adding two of the addends together at a time, the answer rotates between even and odd. When the final two numbers are added together, one is even and the other odd. Therefore, the sum is odd, which makes the product odd since it is equivalent to the sum.

    Using the problem 5×15, students may also use the dot method.

    ```
    •••••••      •••••••      •••••••      •••••••      •••••••
           +            +            +            +
    ••••••••     ••••••••     ••••••••     ••••••••     ••••••••
    ```

    After students circle the pairs of dots, one dot from each set of 15 remains, for a total of 5 dots. Students can group these together and circle more pairs, as shown below.

    ∞∞•

    Since there is still one dot remaining, the product of two odd numbers is odd.

Lesson 16:   Even and Odd Numbers

6. **The product of an even number and an odd number is even.**

Answers will vary, but one example is provided.

Using the problem 6×7, students know that this is equivalent to the sum of six sevens, or $7 + 7 + 7 + 7 + 7 + 7$. Students also know that the sum of two odd numbers is even, and the sum of two even numbers is even. Therefore, when adding two addends at a time, the result is an even number. The sum of these even numbers is also even, which means the total sum is even. This also implies the product is even since the sum and product are equivalent.

Using the problem 6×7, students may also use the dot method.

$$\begin{matrix} \bullet\bullet\bullet \\ \bullet\bullet\bullet\bullet \end{matrix} + \begin{matrix} \bullet\bullet\bullet \\ \bullet\bullet\bullet\bullet \end{matrix} + \begin{matrix} \bullet\bullet\bullet \\ \bullet\bullet\bullet\bullet \end{matrix} + \begin{matrix} \bullet\bullet\bullet \\ \bullet\bullet\bullet\bullet \end{matrix} + \begin{matrix} \bullet\bullet\bullet \\ \bullet\bullet\bullet\bullet \end{matrix} + \begin{matrix} \bullet\bullet\bullet \\ \bullet\bullet\bullet\bullet \end{matrix}$$

After students circle the pairs of dots, one dot from each set of 7 remains, for a total of 6 dots. Students can group these together and circle more pairs, as shown below.

Since there are no dots remaining, the product of an even number and an odd number is even.

After students complete their posters, hang the posters up around the room. Conduct a gallery walk to let groups examine each poster and take notes in their student materials. In the end, students should have a proof for all three exercises in their student handbook.

Allow time for a discussion and an opportunity for students to ask questions.

Closing (5 minutes)

- How does knowing whether a sum or product is even or odd assist in division?
  - *Possible student response: When dividing, it helps to know whether the sum or product of two numbers is even or odd because it narrows down the possible factors. For example, if a dividend is odd, then we know the factors must also be odd because the product of two odd numbers is odd.*

Lesson Summary

Adding:

- The sum of two even numbers is even.
- The sum of two odd numbers is even.
- The sum of an even number and an odd number is odd.

Multiplying:

- The product of two even numbers is even.
- The product of two odd numbers is odd.
- The product of an even number and an odd number is even.

Exit Ticket (5 minutes)

Lesson 16: Even and Odd Numbers

Name _____   Date _____

Exit Ticket

Determine whether each sum or product is even or odd. Explain your reasoning.

1. $56,426 + 17,895$

2. $317,362 \times 129,324$

3. $10,481 + 4,569$

4. $32,457 \times 12,781$

5.   Show or explain why $12 + 13 + 14 + 15 + 16$ results in an even sum.

Exit Ticket Sample Solutions

Determine whether each sum or product is even or odd. Explain your reasoning.

1. $56,426 + 17,895$

    The sum is odd because the sum of an even number and an odd number is odd.

2. $317,362 \times 129,324$

    The product is even because the product of two even numbers is even.

3. $104,81 + 4,569$

    The sum is even because the sum of two odd numbers is even.

4. $32,457 \times 12,781$

    The product is odd because the product of two odd numbers is odd.

5. **Show or explain why $12 + 13 + 14 + 15 + 16$ results in an even sum.**

    $12 + 13$ is odd because even + odd is odd.

    Odd number + 14 is odd because odd + even is odd.

    Odd number + 15 is even because odd + odd is even.

    Even number + 16 is even because even + even is even.

    OR

    Students may group even numbers together, $12 + 14 + 16$, which results in an even number. Then, when students combine the two odd numbers, $13 + 15$, the result is another even number. We know that the sum of two evens results in another even number.

Problem Set Sample Solutions

Without solving, tell whether each sum or product is even or odd. Explain your reasoning.

1. $346 + 721$

    The sum is odd because the sum of an even and an odd number is odd.

2. $4,690 \times 141$

    The product is even because the product of an even and an odd number is even.

3. $1,462,891 \times 745,629$

    The product is odd because the product of two odd numbers is odd.

Lesson 16:   Even and Odd Numbers

4. $425,922 + 32,481,064$

The sum is even because the sum of two even numbers is even.

5. $32 + 45 + 67 + 91 + 34 + 56$

The first two addends are odd because an even and an odd is odd.

Odd number $+67$ is even because the sum of two odd numbers is even.

Even number $+91$ is odd because the sum of an even and an odd number is odd.

Odd number $+34$ is odd because the sum of an odd and an even number is odd.

Odd number $+56$ is odd because the sum of an odd and an even number is odd.

Therefore, the final sum is odd.

Lesson 16:   Even and Odd Numbers

EUREKA MATH

Lesson 17: Divisibility Tests for 3 and 9

Student Outcomes

- Students apply divisibility rules, specifically for 3 and 9, to understand factors and multiples.

Lesson Notes

Students already have knowledge on the divisibility rules of 2, 4, 5, 8, and 10. Although those rules are not a focus for this lesson, they are revisited throughout the lesson. Also, emphasize the difference between factors and multiples throughout the lesson.

Classwork

Opening Exercise (5 minutes)

The Opening Exercise helps students review the divisibility tests for the numbers 2, 4, 5, 8, and 10.

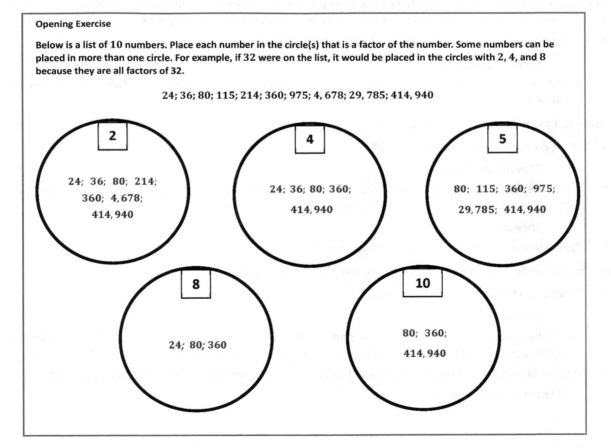

Opening Exercise

Below is a list of 10 numbers. Place each number in the circle(s) that is a factor of the number. Some numbers can be placed in more than one circle. For example, if 32 were on the list, it would be placed in the circles with 2, 4, and 8 because they are all factors of 32.

24; 36; 80; 115; 214; 360; 975; 4,678; 29,785; 414,940

2

24; 36; 80; 214; 360; 4,678; 414,940

4

24; 36; 80; 360; 414,940

5

80; 115; 360; 975; 29,785; 414,940

8

24; 80; 360

10

80; 360; 414,940

© 2015 Great Minds. eureka-math.org
G6-M2-TE-B2-1.3.1-01.2016

Discussion (8 minutes)

Discuss students' results from the Opening Exercise. Have students share their answers, or the teacher can conduct a poll (raising hands, standing up, electronically) to determine where students placed each number.

MP.3

After sharing which numbers belong in each circle, have students examine the numbers in the Opening Exercise. Ask students to find rules to determine in which group the number belongs just by looking at it.

Ask students to discuss the divisibility rules for each number, and have them take notes in their materials

MP.8

Discussion

- Divisibility rule for 2: *If and only if its unit digit is* 0, 2, 4, 6, *or* 8
- Divisibility rule for 4: *If and only if its last two digits are a number divisible by* 4
- Divisibility rule for 5: *If and only if its unit digit is* 0 *or* 5
- Divisibility rule for 8: *If and only if its last three digits are a number divisible by* 8
- Divisibility rule for 10: *If and only if its unit digit is* 0
- Decimal numbers with fraction parts do not follow the divisibility tests.

Students learn two new divisibility rules today. The rules are used to determine if numbers are divisible by 3 or 9. Start with students who already know the factors of 3 and 9, so they can see that the rule works.

- What do the numbers 12, 18, 30, 66, and 93 all have in common?
  - *Each is divisible by* 3.
- Calculate the sum of the digits for each given number. For example, the sum of the digits in the number 12 is 3 because $1 + 2 = 3$.

Give students time to find the sums. Record the sums on the board.

- What do these sums have in common?
  - *They are divisible by* 3.
- When the sum of a number's digits is divisible by 3, the entire number is divisible by 3. Now let's examine a different set of numbers: 27, 36, 54, 72, and 99. What do these numbers have in common?
  - *They are divisible by* 9.
- Calculate the sum of the digits for each given number.

Provide time for students to find the sums. Record the sums on the board.

- What do all the sums have in common?
  - *They are divisible by* 9.
- When the sum of the digits is divisible by 3 and 9, the entire number is divisible by 9. Let's use this knowledge to determine if a large number is divisible by 3, 9, or both. The number 765 is divisible by both 3 and 9.
- We can use what we know about the distributive property to prove that 765 is divisible by 3 and by 9.
- Let's begin by expanding 765.

Display the following progression.

- We can represent 765 as:

$$7 \times 100 + 6 \times 10 + 5 \times 1$$

- We can further decompose the numbers that are easily seen as divisible by 3 and 9.

- Let's decompose 100 to 99 + 1. Why would we do this?

  □ *Because we already know that* 99 *is divisible by* 3 *and* 9.

$$7(99 + 1) + 6 \times 10 + 5$$

- We can also decompose 10 to 9 + 1. Why would we do this?

  □ *Because we already know that* 9 *is divisible by* 3 *and* 9.

$$7(99 + 1) + 6(9 + 1) + 5$$

- Let's use the distributive property further to distribute the factor 7 in the expression. We can represent 7 times the quantity (99 + 1) as $7(99) + 7 \times 1$, or $7(99) + 7$.

$$7(99) + 7 + 6(9 + 1) + 5$$

- We can distribute the factor 6 in the same fashion. How can we distribute the factor 6 in the expression?

  □ *We can represent* 6 *times the quantity* $(9 + 1)$ *as* $6(9) + 6 \times 1$ *or* $6(9) + 6$.

  □ $7(99) + 7 + 6(9) + 6 + 5$

- Since we know that 9 is divisible by both 3 and 9, let's factor the 9 out of the expression. We can use the commutative and associative properties to easily see this.

$$7(99) + 7 + 6(9) + 6 + 5$$
$$7(9 \times 11) + 6(9 \times 1) + 7 + 6 + 5$$
$$9(7 \times 11 + 6) + 7 + 6 + 5$$

- Let's investigate our current expression. Obviously the product of $9(7 \times 11 + 6)$ is divisible by 9 since the 9 is already factored out.

- What about the sum of 7 + 6 + 5? What is the sum? Is this sum divisible by 3 and 9?

  □ $7 + 6 + 5 = 18$.

  □ *This sum is divisible by* 3 *and* 9.

- Are 3 and 9 both factors of 18?

  □ *Yes*

- What do you notice about the addends 7 + 6 + 5?

  □ *They are the digits of our original number* 765.

- Let's look once more at the expression:

$$9(7 \times 11 + 6) + 7 + 6 + 5$$
$$9(7 \times 11 + 6) + 18$$

both divisible by 3 and 9

- Since the first term is divisible by 3 and 9, the number 765 is divisible by 3 and 9 if and only if 7 + 6 + 5 is also divisible by 3 and 9.

- This process can be used for any decimal whole number!

© 2015 Great Minds. eureka-math.org
G6-M2-TE-B2-1.3.1-012016

Introduce the divisibility rules for 3 and 9. Have students record the rules in their student materials.

> - **Divisibility rule for 3:** *If the sum of the digits is divisible by 3, then the number is divisible by 3.*
> - **Divisibility rule for 9:** *If the sum of the digits is divisible by 9, then the number is divisible by 9.*

Through further discussion, explain to students that if a number is divisible by 9, it is also divisible by 3; but if a number is divisible by 3, it is not necessarily divisible by 9.

- Because $9 = 3 \times 3$, any number that is divisible by 9 is also divisible by 3.

Example 1 (5 minutes)

Example 1

This example shows how to apply the two new divisibility rules we just discussed.

Explain why 378 is divisible by 3 and 9.

  a. **Expand 378.**

   $300 + 70 + 8$

   $3 \times 100 + 7 \times 10 + 8$

  b. **Decompose the expression to factor by 9.**

   $3(99 + 1) + 7(9 + 1) + 8$

   $3(99) + 3 + 7(9) + 7 + 8$

  c. **Factor the 9.**

   $3(9 \times 11) + 3 + 7(9 \times 1) + 7 + 8$

   $9(3 \times 11 + 7) + 3 + 7 + 8$

  d. **What is the sum of the three digits?**

   $3 + 7 + 8 = 18$; *the sum of the three digits is* 18.

  e. **Is 18 divisible by 9?**

   Yes

  f. **Is the entire number 378 divisible by 9? Why or why not?**

   The number 378 is divisible by 9 because the sum of the digits is divisible by 9.

> **Scaffolding:**
> - If needed, the teacher can also ask if 18 is divisible by 3. Students may still struggle with the connection between the multiples of 3 and 9.
> - If students struggled with the Opening Exercise, the divisibility rules for 2, 4, 5, 8, and 10 can be reviewed in this example as well.

This may be the place to help students recognize the difference between factors and multiples. Nine is a factor of 378 because it is the product of 9 and 42; therefore, 378 is a multiple of 9.

MP.7

EUREKA
MATH

> g. Is the number 378 divisible by 3? Why or why not?
>
> *Three is a factor of* 378 *because if* 9 *is a factor of* 378, *then* 3 *will also be a factor. OR*
>
> *The number* 378 *is divisible by* 3 *because the sum of the digits is divisible by* 3.

Example 2 (5 minutes)

The students have now seen one example of the two new divisibility rules. Allow students to work with a partner to decide whether a given number is divisible by 3 and 9. If a majority of students are still struggling, ask the same leading questions found in Example 1.

- Is 3,822 divisible by 3 or 9? Why or why not?

Encourage students to check 9 first because if 9 is a factor, then students know that 3 is also a factor. If 3,822 is not divisible by 9, then students must check to see if 3,822 is divisible by 3.

- *The number* 3,822 *is divisible by* 3 *but not by* 9 *because the sum of the digits is* $3 + 8 + 2 + 2$, *which equals* 15, *and* 15 *is divisible by* 3 *but not by* 9.

Example 2

Is 3,822 divisible by 3 or 9? Why or why not?

The number 3,822 *is divisible by* 3 *but not by* 9 *because the sum of the digits is* $3 + 8 + 2 + 2 = 15$, *and* 15 *is divisible by* 3 *but not by* 9.

This is another opportunity to emphasize the difference between factors and multiples. Three is a factor of 3,822 because the product of 3 and 1,274 is 3,822; therefore, 3,822 is a multiple of 3.

Exercises 1–5 (13 minutes)

Students may work with partners or individually to complete the exercises. Remind students that they may circle more than one answer.

Exercises 1–5

Circle ALL the numbers that are factors of the given number. Complete any necessary work in the space provided.

1. 2,838 is divisible by

    (3)

    9

    4

Explain your reasoning for your choice(s).

The number 2,838 *is divisible by* 3 *because* 3 *is a factor of* 2,838. *I know this because the sum of the digits is* 21, *which is divisible by* 3. *The number* 2,838 *is not divisible by* 9 *because* 21 *is not divisible by* 9, *and* 2,838 *is not divisible by* 4 *because the last two digits* (38) *are not divisible by* 4.

---

2.   34,515 is divisible by

Explain your reasoning for your choice(s).

The number 34,515 is divisible by 3 and 9 because both 3 and 9 are factors of 34,515. I know this because the sum of the digits is 18, and 18 is divisible by both 3 and 9. The number 34,515 is also divisible by 5 because the unit digit is a 5.

3.   10,534,341 is divisible by

Explain your reasoning for your choice(s).

The number 10,534,341 is divisible by 3 but not 9 because 3 is a factor of 10,534,341, but 9 is not. I know this because the sum of the digits is 21, which is divisible by 3 but not 9. The number 10,534,341 is not divisible by 2 because it does not end with 0, 2, 4, 6, or 8.

4.   4,320 is divisible by

Explain your reasoning for your choice(s).

The number 4,320 is divisible by 3 and 9 because 3 and 9 are factors of 4,320. I know this because the sum of the digits is 9, which is divisible by 3 and 9. The number 4,320 is also divisible by 10 because 10 is a factor of 4,320. I know this because the unit digit is 0.

5.   6,240 is divisible by

Explain your reasoning for your choice(s).

The number 6,240 is divisible by 3 but not divisible by 9 because 3 is a factor of 6,240, but 9 is not. I know this because the sum of the digits is 12, which is divisible by 3 but not divisible by 9. The number 6,240 is divisible by 8 because the last three digits (240) is divisible by 8.

EUREKA MATH

Closing (4 minutes)

- Without completing the division, how can you determine if a number is divisible by 3?
    - *Calculate the sum of the digits; if the sum of the digits is divisible by 3, the entire number is divisible by 3.*
- If a number is divisible by 9, is it divisible by 3? Explain your answer.
    - *If a number is divisible by 9, the sum of the digits is divisible by 9. Any number that is divisible by 9 is also divisible by 3 since 9 = 3 × 3.*
- If a number is divisible by 3, is it divisible by 9? Explain your answer.
    - *If a number is divisible by 3, it may not be divisible by 9 because 3 has more multiples than 9.*

Lesson Summary

To determine if a number is divisible by 3 or 9:

- **Calculate the sum of the digits.**
- **If the sum of the digits is divisible by 3, the entire number is divisible by 3.**
- **If the sum of the digits is divisible by 9, the entire number is divisible by 9.**

Note: If a number is divisible by 9, the number is also divisible by 3.

Exit Ticket (5 minutes)

Lesson 17: Divisibility Tests for 3 and 9

Exit Ticket

1.   Is 26,341 divisible by 3? If it is, write the number as the product of 3 and another factor. If not, explain.

2.   Is 8,397 divisible by 9? If it is, write the number as the product of 9 and another factor. If not, explain.

3.   Explain why 186,426 is divisible by both 3 and 9.

Exit Ticket Sample Solutions

1. Is 26,341 divisible by 3? If it is, write the number as the product of 3 and another factor. If not, explain.

   The number 26,341 is not divisible by 3 because the sum of the digits is 16, which is not divisible by 3.

2. Is 8,397 divisible by 9? If it is, write the number as the product of 9 and another factor. If not, explain.

   The number 8,397 is divisible by 9 because the sum of the digits is 27, which is divisible by 9. Nine is a factor of 8,397 because $9 \times 933 = 8,397$.

3. Explain why 186,426 is divisible by both 3 and 9.

   The number 186,426 is divisible by both 3 and 9 because the sum of the digits is 27, which is divisible by both 3 and 9.

Problem Set Sample Solutions

1. Is 32,643 divisible by both 3 and 9? Why or why not?

   The number 32,643 is divisible by both 3 and 9 because the sum of the digits is 18, which is divisible by 3 and 9.

2. Circle all the factors of 424, 380 from the list below.

           8 9

   ② ③ ④ ⑤ 8 9 ⑩

3. Circle all the factors of 322,875 from the list below.

   2 ③ 4 ⑤ 8 ⑨ 10

4. Write a 3-digit number that is divisible by both 3 and 4. Explain how you know this number is divisible by 3 and 4.

   Answers will vary. Possible student response: The sum of the digits is divisible by 3, and that's how I know the number is divisible by 3. The last 2 digits are divisible by 4, so the entire number is divisible by 4.

5. Write a 4-digit number that is divisible by both 5 and 9. Explain how you know this number is divisible by 5 and 9.

   Answers will vary. Possible student response: The number ends with a 5 or 0, so the entire number is divisible by 5. The sum of the digits is divisible by 9, so the entire number is divisible by 9.

Lesson 18: Least Common Multiple and Greatest Common Factor

Student Outcomes

- Students find the least common multiple and greatest common factor and apply knowledge of factors to use the distributive property.

Lesson Notes

Least common multiple and greatest common factor are terms that are easily confused by young learners. A clear definition of both phrases with several examples of each should be posted in the classroom before, during, and after the lesson. Furthermore, these skills should be practiced regularly so that the concepts do not fade or blend together from lack of use.

During this lesson, students move around in groups to various stations where a topic is presented on chart paper. At each station, students read the directions, choose a problem, and then work collaboratively to solve the problem. Group students prior to the lesson using the most appropriate ability or social grouping.

There are four different topics: Factors and GCF, Multiples and LCM, Using Prime Factors to Determine GCF, and Applying Factors to the Distributive Property.

Use two sets of chart paper for each topic to create eight stations. This makes manageable groups of 3 or 4 students. Place the stations in order around the room (1, 2, 3, 4, 1, 2, 3, 4) so that it does not matter where a group starts and so that each group finishes after only three rotations. Groups should spend five minutes at each station.

Suggested Student Roles:

Marker	This student records the group's work on the chart paper. Note: Each group should use a different (unique) color when adding its work to the chart paper.
Recorder	This student records the group's work in his student materials and later shares this work with the other members of the group, ensuring that all students finish the activity with their student materials completed.
Calculator Operator/Master Mathematician	This student uses a calculator when necessary and helps clarify the group's response.

Materials

Eight pieces of chart paper with directions attached, one calculator per group, a different colored chart marker for each group, a multiplication table posted at Stations 2 and 4.

Classwork

Opening (4 minutes)

Point out the definitions on the student pages, and work through the examples before assigning and releasing groups.

> The *greatest common factor* of two whole numbers (not both zero) is the greatest whole number that is a factor of each number. The greatest common factor of two whole numbers a and b is denoted by GCF (a, b).
>
> The *least common multiple* of two whole numbers is the smallest whole number greater than zero that is a multiple of each number. The least common multiple of two whole numbers a and b is denoted by LCM (a, b).

Example 1 (3 minutes): Greatest Common Factor

Example 1: Greatest Common Factor

Find the greatest common factor of 12 and 18.

- Listing the factor pairs in order helps ensure that no common factors are missed. Start with 1 multiplied by the number.

- Circle all factors that appear on both lists.

- Place a triangle around the greatest of these common factors.

GCF (12, 18)   6

12

1	12
2	6
3	4

18

1	18
2	9
3	6

© 2015 Great Minds. eureka-math.org
G6-M2-TE-B2-1.3.1-01.2016

EUREKA
MATH

Example 2 (5 minutes): Least Common Multiple

> *Scaffolding:*
>
> Multiplication tables should be used by students with automaticity issues. Naming this a "Multiples Table" is also effective with some students.

Example 2: Least Common Multiple

Find the least common multiple of 12 and 18.

LCM (12, 18)

Write the first 10 multiples of 12.

12, 24, 36, 48, 60, 72, 84, 96, 108, 120

Write the first 10 multiples of 18.

18, 36, 54, 72, 90, 108, 126, 144, 162, 180

Circle the multiples that appear on both lists.

12, 24, (36), 48, 60, (72), 84, 96, (108), 120

18, (36), 54, (72), 90, (108), 126, 144, 162, 180

Put a rectangle around the least of these common multiples.

12, 24, [(36)], 48, 60, (72), 84, 96, (108), 120

18, [(36)], 54, (72), 90, (108), 126, 144, 162, 180

- Is it really necessary to write out 10 multiples of each number?
  - *No, we could have stopped as soon as a multiple appeared on both lists.*
- Should we start by writing the multiples of the larger or the smaller of the two numbers? Which leads us to finding the LCM most efficiently?
  - *If we start writing the multiples of the larger of the two numbers, we can stop when we find thefirst one that is a multiple of the smaller of the two numbers. In the example given, we would list the multiples of 18 first and stop at 36 because 36 is a multiple of 12. Using that method, we would have found the LCM (12,18) after listing only two numbers.*

Discussion (5 minutes)

- Today, groups visit several stations around the room. Each group has five minutes at each station to read and follow directions. Use only the Recorder's paper at the station. Later, the Recorder shares his copy of the work, so everyone leaves with a record of today's classwork.
- Another person in the group, the Marker, has the chart marker for writing on the chart paper, and a third person serves as Calculator Operator/Master Mathematician, who uses a calculator when necessary and helps to clarify the group's response before putting it on the chart paper.
- At each station, the directions start the same way: Choose one of the problems that has not yet been solved. Solve it together on the Recorder's page. The Marker should copy your group's work neatly on the chart paper and cross out the problem your group solved so that the next group solves a different problem.

EUREKA MATH

Exercises (20 minutes; 5 minutes per station)

Station 1: Factors and GCF

Groups choose from the following number problems:

Find the greatest common factor of one of these pairs: 30, 50; 30, 45; 45, 60; 42, 70; 96, 144.

Next, groups choose one of the following application problems:

a.   There are 18 girls and 24 boys who want to participate in a Trivia Challenge. If each team must have the same ratio of girls and boys, what is the greatest number of teams that can enter? Find how many boys and girls each team would have.

b.   Ski Club members are preparing identical welcome kits for new skiers. The Ski Club has 60 hand-warmer packets and 48 foot-warmer packets. Find the greatest number of identical kits they can prepare using all of the hand-warmer and foot-warmer packets. How many hand-warmer packets and foot-warmer packets would each welcome kit have?

c.   There are 435 representatives and 100 senators serving in the United States Congress. How many identical groups with the same numbers of representatives and senators could be formed from all of Congress if we want the largest groups possible? How many representatives and senators would be in each group?

d.   Is the GCF of a pair of numbers ever equal to one of the numbers? Explain with an example.

e.   Is the GCF of a pair of numbers ever greater than both numbers? Explain with an example.

Station 1: Factors and GCF

Choose one of these problems that has not yet been solved. Solve it together on your student page. Then, use your marker to copy your work neatly on the chart paper. Use your marker to cross out your choice so that the next group solves a different problem.

GCF (30, 50)
Factors of 30: 1, 2, 3, 5, 6, 10, 15, 30   *Factors of 50:* 1, 2, 5, 10, 25, 50
Common Factors: 1, 2, 5, 10   *Greatest Common Factor:* 10

GCF (30, 45)
Factors of 30: 1, 2, 3, 5, 6, 10, 15, 30
Common Factors: 1, 3, 5, 15   *Factors of 45:* 1, 3, 5, 9, 15, 45
                                                      Greatest Common Factor: 15

GCF (45, 60)
Factors of 45: 1, 3, 5, 9, 15, 45
Common Factors: 1, 3, 5, 15   *Factors of 60:* 1, 2, 3, 4, 5, 6, 10, 12, 15, 20, 30, 60
                                                      Greatest Common Factor: 15

GCF (42, 70)
Factors of 42: 1, 2, 3, 6, 7, 14, 21, 42
Common Factors: 1, 2, 7, 14   *Factors of 70:* 1, 2, 5, 7, 10, 14, 35, 70
                                                      Greatest Common Factor: 14

GCF (96,144)
Factors of 96: 1, 2, 3, 4, 6, 8, 12, 16, 24, 32, 48, 96   *Factors of 144:* 1, 2, 3, 4, 6, 8, 9, 12, 16, 18, 24, 36, 48, 72, 144
Common Factors: 1, 2, 3, 4, 6, 8, 12, 16, 24, 48   *Greatest Common Factor :* 48

© 2015 Great Minds. eureka-math.org
G6-M2-TE-B2-1.3.1-01.2016

Next, choose one of these problems that has not yet been solved:

a. There are 18 girls and 24 boys who want to participate in a Trivia Challenge. If each team must have the same ratio of girls and boys, what is the greatest number of teams that can enter? Find how many boys and girls each team would have.

6 teams can enter the Trivia Challenge, each having 3 girls and 4 boys.

b. Ski Club members are preparing identical welcome kits for new skiers. The Ski Club has 60 hand-warmer packets and 48 foot-warmer packets. Find the greatest number of identical kits they can prepare using all of the hand-warmer and foot-warmer packets. How many hand-warmer packets and foot-warmer packets would each welcome kit have?

There would be 12 welcome kits, each having 5 hand-warmer packets and 4 foot-warmer packets.

c. There are 435 representatives and 100 senators serving in the United States Congress. How many identical groups with the same numbers of representative and senators could be formed from all of Congress if we want the largest groups possible? How many representatives and senators would be in each group?

5 identical groups with the same numbers of representatives and senators can be formed, each group with 87 representatives and 20 senators.

d. Is the GCF of a pair of numbers ever equal to one of the numbers? Explain with an example.

Yes. Valid examples should show a pair of numbers where the lesser of the two numbers is a factor of the greater number; the greater of the two numbers is a multiple of the lesser number.

e. Is the GCF of a pair of numbers ever greater than both numbers? Explain with an example.

No. Factors are, by definition, less than or equal to the number. Therefore, the GCF cannot be greater than both numbers.

Station 2: Multiples and LCM

Groups choose from the following number problems:

Find the least common multiple of one of these pairs: 9, 12; 8, 18; 4, 30; 12, 30; 20, 50.

Next, groups choose one of the following application problems:

a. Hot dogs come packed 10 in a package. Hot dog buns come packed 8 in a package. If we want one hot dog for each bun for a picnic with none left over, what is the least amount of each we need to buy? How many packages of each item would we have to buy?

b. Starting at 6:00 a.m., a bus stops at my street corner every 15 minutes. Also starting at 6:00 a.m., a taxi cab comes by every 12 minutes. What is the next time both a bus and a taxi are at the corner at the same time?

c. Two gears in a machine are aligned by a mark drawn from the center of one gear to the center of the other. If the first gear has 24 teeth, and the second gear has 40 teeth, how many revolutions of the first gear are needed until the marks line up again?

d. Is the LCM of a pair of numbers ever equal to one of the numbers? Explain with an example.

e. Is the LCM of a pair of numbers ever less than both numbers? Explain with an example.

Station 2: Multiples and LCM

Choose one of these problems that has not yet been solved. Solve it together on your student page. Then, use your marker to copy your work neatly on the chart paper. Use your marker to cross out your choice so that the next group solves a different problem.

LCM (9, 12)
Multiples of 9: 9, 18, 27, 36   *Multiples of 12:* 12, 24, 36
Least Common Multiple: 36

LCM (8, 18)
Multiples of 8: 8, 16, 24, 32, 40, 48, 56, 64, 72   *Multiples of 18:* 18, 36, 54, 72
Least Common Multiple: 72

LCM (4, 30)
Multiples of 4: 4, 8, 12, 16, 20, 24, 28, 32, 36, 40, 44, 48, 52, 56, 60   *Multiples of 30:* 30, 60
Least Common Multiple: 60

LCM (12, 30)
Multiples of 12: 12, 24, 36, 48, 60   *Multiples of 30:* 30, 60
Least Common Multiple: 60

LCM (20, 50)
Multiples of 20: 20, 40, 60, 80, 100   *Multiples of 50:* 50, 100
Least Common Multiple: 100

Next, choose one of these problems that has not yet been solved. Solve it together on your student page. Then, use your marker to copy your work neatly on this chart paper and to cross out your choice so that the next group solves a different problem.

a. Hot dogs come packed 10 in a package. Hot dog buns come packed 8 in a package. If we want one hot dog for each bun for a picnic with none left over, what is the least amount of each we need to buy? How many packages of each item would we have to buy?

   Four packages of hot dogs = 40 hot dogs. Five packages of buns = 40 buns. LCM (8, 10) = 40.

b. Starting at 6:00 a.m., a bus stops at my street corner every 15 minutes. Also starting at 6:00 a.m., a taxi cab comes by every 12 minutes. What is the next time both a bus and a taxi are at the corner at the same time?

   Both a bus and a taxi arrive at the corner at 7:00 a.m., which is 60 minutes after 6:00 a.m. LCM (12,15) = 60.

c. Two gears in a machine are aligned by a mark drawn from the center of one gear to the center of the other. If the first gear has 24 teeth, and the second gear has 40 teeth, how many revolutions of the first gear are needed until the marks line up again?

   The first gear needs five revolutions. During this time, 120 teeth pass by. The second gear revolves three times. LCM (24, 40) = 120.

d. Is the LCM of a pair of numbers ever equal to one of the numbers? Explain with an example.

   Yes. Valid examples should show of a pair of numbers where the lesser of the two numbers is a factor of the greater number; the greater of the two numbers is a multiple of the lesser number.

e. Is the LCM of a pair of numbers ever less than both numbers? Explain with an example.

   No. Multiples are, by definition, equal to or greater than the number.

Station 3: Using Prime Factors to Determine GCF

Note: If the classroom has Internet access, a Factor Tree applet is available at
http://nlvm.usu.edu/en/nav/frames_asid_202_g_3_t_1.html?from=category_g_3_t_1.html

Choose "Two Factor Trees" and "User Defined Problems." When both numbers are factored into prime factors, each common prime factor is dragged into the middle of a two-circle Venn diagram. Unique prime factors are separated into the other two regions of the Venn diagram. Introducing the applet before the lesson and allowing exploration time should strengthen understanding and make this lesson more cohesive.

Groups choose from the following number problems:

Use prime factors to find the greatest common factor of one of the following pairs of numbers:
30, 50; 30, 45; 45, 60; 42, 70; 96, 144.

Next, groups choose one of the following application problems:

a. Would you rather find all the factors of a number or find all the prime factors of a number? Why?

b. Find the GCF of your original pair of numbers.

c. Is the product of your LCM and GCF less than, greater than, or equal to the product of your numbers?

d. Glenn's favorite number is very special because it reminds him of the day his daughter, Sarah, was born. The prime factors of this number do not repeat, and all of the prime numbers are less than 12. What is Glenn's number? When was Sarah born?

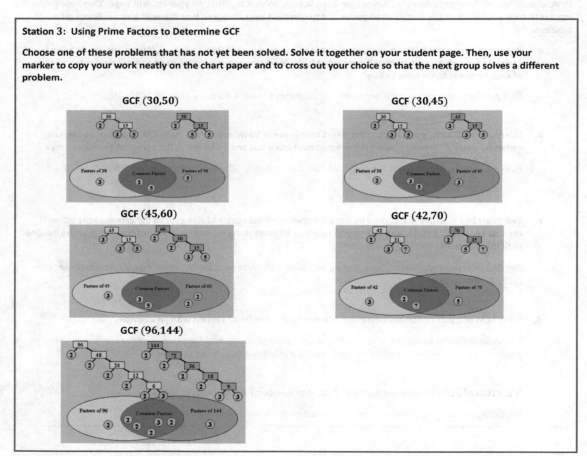

Station 3: Using Prime Factors to Determine GCF

Choose one of these problems that has not yet been solved. Solve it together on your student page. Then, use your marker to copy your work neatly on the chart paper and to cross out your choice so that the next group solves a different problem.

GCF (30,50)   GCF (30,45)

GCF (45,60)   GCF (42,70)

GCF (96,144)

Next, choose one of these problems that has not yet been solved:

a. Would you rather find all the factors of a number or find all the prime factors of a number? Why?

   Accept opinions. Students should defend their answer and use accurate mathematical terms in their response.

b. Find the GCF of your original pair of numbers.

   See answers listed in Exploratory Challenge 1.

c. Is the product of your LCM and GCF less than, greater than, or equal to the product of your numbers?

   In all cases, GCF $(a, b) \cdot$ LCM $(a, b) = a \cdot b$.

d. Glenn's favorite number is very special because it reminds him of the day his daughter, Sarah, was born. The factors of this number do not repeat, and all of the prime numbers are less than 12. What is Glenn's number? When was Sarah born?

   $2 \cdot 3 \cdot 5 \cdot 7 \cdot 11 = 2{,}310$ *Sarah's birthdate is 2/3/10.*

Station 4: Applying Factors to the Distributive Property

Study these examples of how factors apply to the distributive property.

MP.7

$$8 + 12 = 4(2) + 4(3) = 4(2 + 3) = 20$$
$$4(2) + 4(3) = 4(5) = 20$$

$$15 + 25 = 5(3) + 5(5) = 5(3 + 5) = 40$$
$$5(3) + 5(5) = 5(8) = 40$$

$$36 - 24 = 4(9) - 4(6) = 4(9-6) = 12$$
$$4(9) - 4(6) = 4(3) = 12$$

Have students factor out the GCF from the two numbers and rewrite the sum using the distributive property.

Groups choose one of the following problems:

a. $12 + 18 =$
b. $42 + 14 =$
c. $36 + 27 =$
d. $16 + 72 =$
e. $44 + 33 =$

Next, students add their own examples to one of two statements applying factors to the distributive property:

$n (a) + n (b) = n (a + b)$

$n (a) - n (b) = n (a - b)$

Station 4: Applying Factors to the Distributive Property

Choose one of these problems that has not yet been solved. Solve it together on your student page. Then, use your marker to copy your work neatly on the chart paper and to cross out your choice so that the next group solves a different problem.

Find the GCF from the two numbers, and rewrite the sum using the distributive property.

1. $12 + 18 =$

    $6(2) + 6(3) = 6(2 + 3) = 6(5) = 30$

2. $42 + 14 =$

    $7(6) + 7(2) = 7(6 + 2) = 7(8) = 56$

3. $36 + 27 =$

    $9(4) + 9(3) = 9(4 + 3) = 9(7) = 63$

4. $16 + 72 =$

    $8(2) + 8(9) = 8(2 + 9) = 8(11) = 88$

5. $44 + 33 =$

    $11(4) + 11(3) = 11(4 + 3) = 11(7) = 77$

Next, add another example to one of these two statements applying factors to the distributive property.

Choose any numbers for *n, a,* and *b*.

$n(a) + n(b) = n(a + b)$

Accept all mathematically correct responses.

$n(a) - n(b) = n(a - b)$

The distributive property holds for addition as well as subtraction. Accept all mathematically correct responses.

Closing (4 minutes)

▪   Use this time to discuss each station. Assign the Problem Set, which asks students to revisit each topic independently.

Exit Ticket (4 minutes)

Lesson 18:   Least Common Multiple and Greatest Common Factor

EUREKA
MATH

Name _____   Date _____

Lesson 18: Least Common Multiple and Greatest Common Factor

Exit Ticket

1. Find the LCM and GCF of 12 and 15.

2. Write two numbers, neither of which is 8, whose GCF is 8.

3. Write two numbers, neither of which is 28, whose LCM is 28.

Rate each of the stations you visited today. Use this scale:

3—Easy—I've got it; I don't need any help.

2—Medium—I need more practice, but I understand some of it.

1—Hard—I'm not getting this yet.

Complete the following chart:

Station	Rating (3,2,1)	Comment to the Teacher
Station 1: Factors and GCF		
Station 2: Multiples and LCM		
Station 3: Using Prime Factors for GCF		
Station 4: Applying Factors to the Distributive Property		

© 2015 Great Minds. eureka-math.org
G6-M2-TE-B2-1.3.1-01.2016

Exit Ticket Sample Solutions

1. Find the LCM and GCF of 12 and 15.

   LCM: 60; GCF: 3

2. Write two numbers, neither of which is 8, whose GCF is 8.

   Answers will vary (e.g., 16 and 24, or 24 and 32).

3. Write two numbers, neither of which is 28, whose LCM is 28.

   Answers will vary (e.g., 4 and 14, or 4 and 7).

Rate each of the stations you visited today. Use this scale:

3—Easy—I've got it, I don't need any help.

2—Medium—I need more practice, but I understand some of it.

1—Hard—I'm not getting this yet.

Complete the following chart:

Station	Rating (3, 2, 1)	Comment to the Teacher
Station 1 Factors and GCF		
Station 2 Multiples and LCM		
Station 3 Using Prime Factors for GCF		
Station 4 Applying Factors to the Distributive Property		

Problem Set Sample Solutions

Students should complete the remaining stations from class.

EUREKA
MATH

Station 1: Factors and GCF

Choose one of these problems that has not yet been solved. Solve it together on your student page. Then, use your marker to copy your work neatly on the chart paper and to cross out your choice so that the next group solves a different problem.

Find the greatest common factor of one of these pairs: 30, 50; 30, 45; 45, 60; 42, 70; 96, 144.

Next, choose one of these problems that has not yet been solved:

a. There are 18 girls and 24 boys who want to participate in a Trivia Challenge. If each team must have the same ratio of girls and boys, what is the greatest number of teams that can enter? Find how many boys and girls each team would have.

b. Ski Club members are preparing identical welcome kits for new skiers. The Ski Club has 60 hand-warmer packets and 48 foot-warmer packets. Find the greatest number of identical kits they can prepare using all of the hand-warmer and foot-warmer packets. How many hand-warmer packets and foot-warmer packets would each welcome kit have?

c. There are 435 representatives and 100 senators serving in the United States Congress. How many identical groups with the same numbers of representatives and senators could be formed from all of Congress if we want the largest groups possible? How many representatives and senators would be in each group?

d. Is the GCF of a pair of numbers ever equal to one of the numbers? Explain with an example.

e. Is the GCF of a pair of numbers ever greater than both numbers? Explain with an example.

Station 2: Multiples and LCM

Choose one of these problems that has not yet been solved. Solve it together on your student page. Then, use your marker to copy your work neatly on the chart paper and to cross out your choice so that the next group solves a different problem.

Find the least common multiple of one of these pairs: 9, 12; 8, 18; 4, 30; 12, 30; 20, 50.

Next, choose one of these problems that has not yet been solved:

a.   Hot dogs come packed 10 in a package. Hot dog buns come packed 8 in a package. If we want one hot dog for each bun for a picnic, with none left over, what is the least amount of each we need to buy? How many packages of each item would we have to buy?

b.   Starting at 6:00 a.m., a bus stops at my street corner every 15 minutes. Also starting at 6:00 a.m., a taxi cab comes by every 12 minutes. What is the next time both a bus and a taxi are at the corner at the same time?

c.   Two gears in a machine are aligned by a mark drawn from the center of one gear to the center of the other. If the first gear has 24 teeth, and the second gear has 40 teeth, how many revolutions of the first gear are needed until the marks line up again?

d.   Is the LCM of a pair of numbers ever equal to one of the numbers? Explain with an example.

e.   Is the LCM of a pair of numbers ever less than both numbers? Explain with an example.

Solve it together on your student page. Then, use your marker to copy your work neatly on this chart paper and to cross out your choice so that the next group solves a different problem.

© 2015 Great Minds. eureka-math.org
G6-M2-TE-B2-1.3.1-01.2016

Station 3: Using Prime Factors to Determine GCF

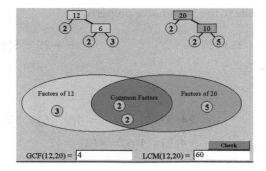

Choose one of these problems that has not yet been solved. Solve it together on your student page. Then, use your marker to copy your work neatly on the chart paper and to cross out your choice so that the next group solves a different problem.

Use prime factors to find the greatest common factor of one of the following pairs of numbers:

30, 50   30, 45   45, 60   42, 70   96, 144.

Next, choose one of these problems that has not yet been solved:

a.   Would you rather find all the factors of a number or find all the prime factors of a number? Why?

b.   Find the GCF of your original pair of numbers.

c.   Is the product of your LCM and GCF less than, greater than, or equal to the product of your numbers?

d.   Glenn's favorite number is very special because it reminds him of the day his daughter, Sarah, was born. The factors of this number do not repeat, and all of the prime numbers are less than 12. What is Glenn's number? When was Sarah born?

Station 4: Applying Factors to the Distributive Property

Study these examples of how factors apply to the distributive property.

$$8 + 12 = 4(2) + 4(3) = 4(2 + 3) = 20 \qquad 15 + 25 = 5(3) + 5(5) = 5(3 + 5) = 40$$

$$4(2) + 4(3) = 4(5) = 20 \qquad\qquad\qquad 5(3) + 5(5) = 5(8) = 40$$

$$36 - 24 = 4(9) - 4(6) = 4(9 - 6) = 12$$

$$4(9) - 4(6) = 4(3) = 12$$

Choose one of these problems that has not yet been solved. Solve it together on your student page. Then, use your marker to copy your work neatly on the chart paper and to cross out your choice so that the next group solves a different problem.

Find the GCF from the two numbers, and rewrite the sum using the distributive property.

1. $12 + 18 =$

2. $42 + 14 =$

3. $36 + 27 =$

4. $16 + 72 =$

5. $44 + 33 =$

Next, add another example to one of these two statements applying factors to the distributive property.

Choose any numbers for n, a, and b.

$$n(a) + n(b) = n(a + b)$$

$$n(a) - n(b) = n(a - b)$$

Lesson 18:   Least Common Multiple and Greatest Common Factor

EUREKA MATH

Lesson 19: The Euclidean Algorithm as an Application of the Long Division Algorithm

Student Outcomes

- Students explore and discover that Euclid's algorithm is a more efficient means to finding the greatest common factor of larger numbers and determine that Euclid's algorithm is based on long division.

Lesson Notes

MP.7 Students look for and make use of structure, connecting long division to Euclid's algorithm.

Students look for and express regularity in repeated calculations leading to finding the greatest common factor of a pair of numbers.

These steps are contained in the Student Materials and should be reproduced, so they can be displayed throughout the lesson:

Euclid's algorithm is used to find the greatest common factor (GCF) of two whole numbers.

MP.8
1. Divide the larger of the two numbers by the smaller one.

2. If there is a remainder, divide it into the divisor.

3. Continue dividing the last divisor by the last remainder until the remainder is zero.

4. The final divisor is the GCF of the original pair of numbers.

In application, the algorithm can be used to find the side length of the largest square that can be used to completely fill a rectangle without overlap or gaps.

Classwork

Opening (5 minutes)

Discuss the Lesson 18 Problem Set before going on to this lesson.

Opening Exercise (4 minutes)

- There are three division warm-ups on your Student Material page today. Please compute them now. Check your answer to make sure it is reasonable.

Opening Exercise

Euclid's algorithm is used to find the greatest common factor (GCF) of two whole numbers.

1. Divide the larger of the two numbers by the smaller one.
2. If there is a remainder, divide it into the divisor.
3. Continue dividing the last divisor by the last remainder until the remainder is zero.
4. The final divisor is the GCF of the original pair of numbers.

$$383 \div 4 = 95.75 \qquad 432 \div 12 = 36 \qquad 403 \div 13 = 31$$

Discussion (2 minutes)

- The Opening Exercise was meant to recall how to determine the quotient of two numbers using long division. You have practiced the long division algorithm many times. Today's lesson is inspired by Euclid, a Greek mathematician who lived around 300 B.C. He discovered a way to find the greatest common factor of two numbers that is based on long division.

Example 1 (10 minutes): Euclid's Algorithm Conceptualized

- What is the GCF of 60 and 100?
    - 20
- What is the interpretation of the GCF in terms of area? Let's take a look.

Project the following diagram:

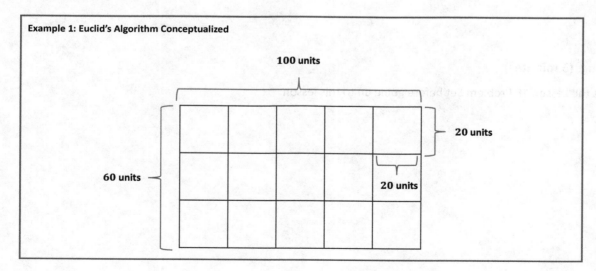

Example 1: Euclid's Algorithm Conceptualized

100 units

60 units

20 units

20 units

- Notice that we can use the GCF of 20 to create the largest square tile that covers the rectangle without any overlap or gaps. We used a 20 × 20 tile.
- But, what if we did not know that? We could start by guessing. What is the biggest square tile that we can guess?
  - 60 × 60

Display the following diagram:

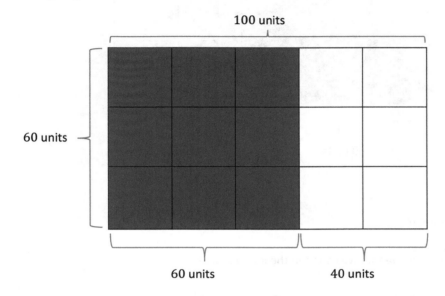

100 units

60 units

60 units   40 units

- It fits, but there are 40 units left over. Do the division problem to prove this.
- What is the leftover area?
  - 60 × 40
- What is the largest square tile that we can fit in the leftover area?
  - 40 × 40

$$\begin{array}{r} 1 \\ 60\overline{)100} \\ -60 \\ \hline 40 \end{array}$$

Note to Teacher:
- With each step in this process, please write out the long division algorithm that accompanies it.
- It is important for students to make a record of this as well. The remainder becomes the new divisor and continues until the remainder is zero.

EUREKA
MATH

Lesson 19:   The Euclidean Algorithm as an Application of the Long Division Algorithm

199

© 2015 Great Minds. eureka-math.org
G6-M2-TE-B2-1.3.1-01.2016

Display the following diagram:

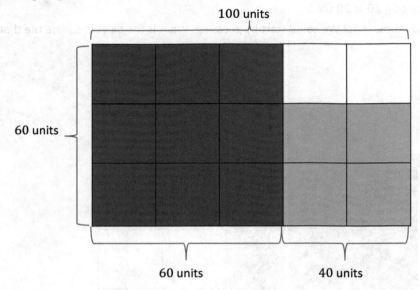

- **What is the leftover area?**
  - 20×40
- **What is the largest square tile that we can fit in the leftover area?**
  - 20×20
- **When we divide 40 by 20, there is no remainder. So, we have tiled the entire rectangle.**
- **If we had started tiling the whole rectangle with squares, the largest square we could have used would be 20 by 20.**

Take a few minutes to allow discussion, questions, and clarification.

$$\begin{array}{r} 2 \\ 20\overline{)40} \\ -40 \\ \hline 0 \end{array}$$

Example 2 (5 minutes): Lesson 18 Classwork Revisited

During Lesson 18, students found the GCF of several pairs of numbers.

- **Let's apply Euclid's algorithm to some of the problems from our last lesson.**

Lesson 19:   The Euclidean Algorithm as an Application of the Long Division Algorithm

EUREKA MATH

Example 2: Lesson 18 Classwork Revisited

a. Let's apply Euclid's algorithm to some of the problems from our last lesson.

   i.   What is the GCF of 30 and 50?

   10

   ii. Using Euclid's algorithm, we follow the steps that are listed in the Opening Exercise.

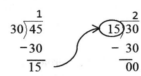

   When the remainder is zero, the final divisor is the GCF.

b. Apply Euclid's algorithm to find the GCF (30, 45).

$$\begin{array}{r} 1 \\ 30\overline{)45} \\ -30 \\ \hline 15 \end{array} \quad\longrightarrow\quad \begin{array}{r} 2 \\ \boxed{15}\overline{)30} \\ -30 \\ \hline 00 \end{array}$$

15

Example 3 (5 minutes): Larger Numbers

Example 3: Larger Numbers

GCF (96, 144)   **GCF (660, 840)**

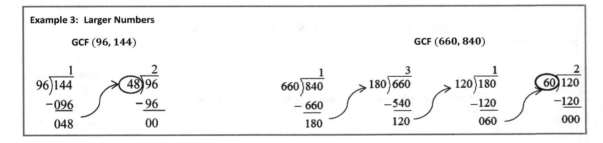

Example 4 (5 minutes): Area Problems

Example 4: Area Problems

The greatest common factor has many uses. Among them, the GCF lets us find out the maximum size of squares that cover a rectangle. When we solve problems like this, we cannot have any gaps or any overlapping squares. Of course, the maximum size squares is the minimum number of squares needed.

A rectangular computer table measures 30 inches by 50 inches. We need to cover it with square tiles. What is the side length of the largest square tile we can use to completely cover the table without overlap or gaps?

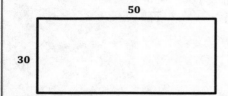
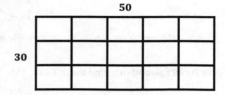

Direct students to consider the GCF (30, 50), which they already calculated. It should become clear that squares of 10 inches by 10 inches should tile the area.

a. If we use squares that are 10 by 10, how many do we need?

$3 \cdot 5$, *or* **15** *squares*

b. If this were a giant chunk of cheese in a factory, would it change the thinking or the calculations we just did?

No

c. How many 10 inch × 10 inch squares of cheese could be cut from the giant 30 inch × 50 inch slab?

15

Scaffolding:

- To find the GCF of two numbers, give students rectangular pieces of paper using the two numbers as length and width (e.g., 6 by 16 cm).
- Challenge students to mark the rectangles into the largest squares possible, cut them up, and stack them to assure their "squareness."
- GCF $(6,16) = 2$

EUREKA MATH

Closing (4 minutes)

- We use Euclid's algorithm to find the GCF of two whole numbers. The steps are listed on your Student Page and need to be followed enough times to get a zero remainder. With practice, this can be a quick method for finding the GCF.

- Let's use the steps to solve this problem: Kiana is creating a quilt made of square patches. The quilt is 48 inches in length and 36 inches in width. What is the largest size of square length of each patch?

- Divide the larger of the two numbers by the smaller one. What is the quotient?
  - □ 1

- If there is a remainder, divide it into the divisor. What is the remainder?
  - □ 12

- What is the divisor?
  - □ 36

- Divide 36 by 12. What is the quotient?
  - □ 3

- Continue dividing the last divisor by the last remainder until the remainder is zero. Is the remainder zero?
  - □ *Yes*

- The final divisor is the GCF of the original pair of numbers. What is the final divisor?
  - □ 12

> **Scaffolding:**
>
> Ask students to compare the process of Euclid's algorithm with a subtraction-only method of finding the GCF:
>
> 1. List the two numbers.
> 2. Find their difference.
> 3. Keep the smaller of the two numbers; discard the larger.
> 4. Use the smaller of the two numbers and the difference to form a new pair.
> 5. Repeat until the two numbers are the same. This is the GCF.
>
> Teacher resource:
>
> http://www.youtube.com/watch?v=2HsIpFAXvKk

Exit Ticket (5 minutes)

Name _____ Date _____

Lesson 19: The Euclidean Algorithm as an Application of the Long Division Algorithm

Exit Ticket

Use Euclid's algorithm to find the greatest common factor of 45 and 75.

Exit Ticket Sample Solutions

Use Euclid's algorithm to find the greatest common factor of 45 and 75.

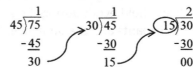

$GCF\ (45, 75) = 15$

Problem Set Sample Solutions

1. Use Euclid's algorithm to find the greatest common factor of the following pairs of numbers:

    a. GCF $(12, 78)$

$$
\begin{array}{r}
6 \\
12\overline{)78} \\
-72 \\
\hline
06
\end{array}
\qquad
\begin{array}{r}
2 \\
6\overline{)12} \\
-12 \\
\hline
00
\end{array}
$$

    $GCF\ (12, 78) = 6$

    b. GCF $(18, 176)$

$$
\begin{array}{r}
9 \\
18\overline{)176} \\
-162 \\
\hline
014
\end{array}
\quad
\begin{array}{r}
1 \\
14\overline{)18} \\
-14 \\
\hline
04
\end{array}
\quad
\begin{array}{r}
3 \\
4\overline{)14} \\
-12 \\
\hline
02
\end{array}
\quad
\begin{array}{r}
2 \\
2\overline{)4} \\
-4 \\
\hline
0
\end{array}
$$

    $GCF\ (18, 176) = 2$

2. Juanita and Samuel are planning a pizza party. They order a rectangular sheet pizza that measures 21 inches by 36 inches. They tell the pizza maker not to cut it because they want to cut it themselves.

    a. All pieces of pizza must be square with none left over. What is the side length of the largest square pieces into which Juanita and Samuel can cut the pizza?

    $GCF\ (21, 36) = 3$ *They can cut the pizza into 3 inch by 3 inch squares.*

    b. How many pieces of this size can be cut?

    $7 \cdot 12 = 84$ *Juanita and Samuel can cut 84 pieces.*

3. Shelly and Mickelle are making a quilt. They have a piece of fabric that measures 48 inches by 168 inches.

    a. All pieces of fabric must be square with none left over. What is the side length of the largest square pieces into which Shelly and Mickelle can cut the fabric?

    $GCF\ (48, 168) = 24$

    b. How many pieces of this size can Shelly and Mickelle cut?

    $2 \cdot 7 = 14$ *They can cut 14 pieces.*

Name _____   Date _____

1. L.B. Johnson Middle School held a track and field event during the school year. The chess club sold various drink and snack items for the participants and the audience. Altogether, they sold 486 items that totaled $2,673.

   a. If the chess club sold each item for the same price, calculate the price of each item.

   b. Explain the value of each digit in your answer to 1(a) using place value terms.

2. The long-jump pit was recently rebuilt to make it level with the runway. Volunteers provided pieces of wood to frame the pit. Each piece of wood provided measures 6 feet, which is approximately 1.8287 meters.

2.75 meters

9.54 meters

    a. Determine the amount of wood, in meters, needed to rebuild the frame.

    b. How many boards did the volunteers supply? Round your calculations to the nearest hundredth, and then provide the whole number of boards supplied.

3. Andy runs 436.8 meters in 62.08 seconds.

   a. If Andy runs at a constant speed, how far does he run in one second? Give your answer to the nearest tenth of a second.

   b. Use place value, multiplication with powers of 10, or equivalent fractions to explain what is happening mathematically to the decimal points in the divisor and dividend before dividing.

   c. In the following expression, place a decimal point in the divisor and the dividend to create a new problem with the same answer as in 3(a). Then, explain how you know the answer will be the same.

$$4\ 3\ 6\ 8 \div 6\ 2\ 0\ 8$$

4. The PTA created a cross-country trail for the meet.

   a. The PTA placed a trail marker in the ground every four hundred yards. Every nine hundred yards, the PTA set up a water station. What is the shortest distance a runner will have to run to see both a water station and trail marker at the same location?

   Answer: _____ hundred yards

   b. There are 1,760 yards in one mile. About how many miles will a runner have to run before seeing both a water station and trail marker at the same location? Calculate the answer to the nearest hundredth of a mile.

   c. The PTA wants to cover the wet areas of the trail with wood chips. They find that one bag of wood chips covers a $3\frac{1}{2}$-yard section of the trail. If there is a wet section of the trail that is approximately $50\frac{1}{4}$ yards long, how many bags of wood chips are needed to cover the wet section of the trail?

5. The Art Club wants to paint a rectangle-shaped mural to celebrate the winners of the track and field meet. They design a checkerboard background for the mural where they will write the winners' names. The rectangle measures 432 inches in length and 360 inches in width. Apply Euclid's algorithm to determine the side length of the largest square they can use to fill the checkerboard pattern completely without overlap or gaps.

EUREKA MATH

A Progression Toward Mastery

Assessment Task Item		STEP 1 Missing or incorrect answer and little evidence of reasoning or application of mathematics to solve the problem.	STEP 2 Missing or incorrect answer but evidence of some reasoning or application of mathematics to solve the problem.	STEP 3 A correct answer with some evidence of reasoning or application of mathematics to solve the problem, OR an incorrect answer with substantial evidence of solid reasoning or application of mathematics to solve the problem.	STEP 4 A correct answer supported by substantial evidence of solid reasoning or application of mathematics to solve the problem.
1	**a** 6.NS.B.2	Student response is missing or depicts inaccurate operation choice.	Student response is inaccurate and does not represent the correct place value.	Student response is inaccurate through minor calculation errors; however, place value is represented accurately.	Student response is correct. The price of each item is determined as $5.50, where place value is represented accurately.
	b 6.NS.B.2	Student response is incorrect or missing. Place value is not depicted in the response.	Student response depicts place value only in monetary denominations, such as dollars and cents.	Student response depicts place value accurately but makes little to no correlation to monetary denominations.	Student response is accurate. Each place value is labeled accurately and shows correlation to the monetary denominations each place value represents. For example, 5 dollars is labeled with 5 ones and 5 dollars, 50 cents is labeled with 5 tenths and 5 dimes, and the zero in the hundredths place is labeled with zero hundredths and "no pennies."
2	**a** 6.NS.B.3	Student response is incorrect or missing. Student merely includes one length and one side in the calculation.	Student response is incorrect based on place value.	Student response depicts understanding of the addition algorithm, but minor calculation errors hinder the correct sum of 24.58 meters.	Student calculations include all sides of the sand pit. Student applies the standard algorithm of addition of decimals to determine the correct sum of 24.58 meters.

© 2015 Great Minds. eureka-math.org
G6-M2-TE-B2-1.3.1-01.2016

		Student response is incorrect or missing. Calculations disregard place value.	Student response is incorrect and depicts inaccurate place value.	Student response is incorrect. Student rounds the decimal quotient to the nearest hundredth and determines the quotient to be 13.44. Student does not provide the whole number of boards supplied.	Student response is correct. Reasoning is evident through the use of place value. The final response is in terms of a whole number. Student determines that from the calculation of 13.44, the volunteers supplied 14 boards.
	b **6.NS.B.3**				
3	**a** **6.NS.B.3**	Student response is incorrect or missing. Calculations disregard place value.	Student response is incorrect. Response depicts inaccurate place value where the divisor is represented by a whole number, but the dividend remains a decimal.	Student response is correct, but the quotient of 7.03 is not rounded to the nearest tenth. OR Student calculations are incorrect but represent knowledge of place value.	Student response is correct, depicting accurate place value in order to generate a whole number dividend. Calculations are flawless, and the answer, 7.0, is represented to the nearest tenth.
	b **6.NS.B.3**	Student response either incorrectly depicts place value or is missing.	Student response depicts some place value knowledge but not enough to sufficiently describe why and how a whole number divisor is generated.	Student response correctly includes accurate place value through the use of equivalent fractions to demonstrate how to generate a whole number divisor.	Student response is correct and includes multiplying by a power of ten to determine an equivalent fraction with a whole number denominator. Student determines that the quotient of the decimals is equivalent to the quotient of the whole numbers generated through the use of place value.
	c **6.NS.B.3**	Student response is missing.	Student response is incorrect or indicates the same decimal placements from the previous problem.	Student response accurately places decimals in the divisor and dividend with no explanation or justification.	Student response accurately places decimals within the divisor (6.208) and dividend (43.68) to generate a quotient of 7.03 and justifies placement through the use of either place value, powers of ten, or equivalent fractions.
4	**a** **6.NS.B.4**	Student response is incorrect or missing. Response is a result of finding the sum of or the difference between 9 and 4.	Student response is incorrect or is simply the product of 4 and 9 with no justification.	Student response accurately finds the least common multiple of 4 and 9, but the response is determined as 36, instead of 36 hundred or 3,600 yards, or the correct response reflects finding the LCM of 400 and 900.	Student response is accurately determined through finding the least common multiple. The response represents an understanding of the unit "hundred" as a means of efficiently determining LCM using 4 and 9, instead of 400 and 900.

Module 2:   Arithmetic Operations Including Division of Fractions

	b 6.NS.B.2	Student response is missing. OR Student response utilizes incorrect operations, such as addition, subtraction, or multiplication.	Student response shows little reasoning through the use of division to determine the quotient. Student response depicts division of 1,760 yards by a divisor of 2, derived from counting the two stations. Student response does not include values from the previous problem.	Student response is incorrect but does include values from the previous problem. Instead of using 3,600, however, the response chooses 36 as the dividend, resulting in an incorrect quotient.	Student response is computed accurately, and the solution is appropriately rounded to the hundredths place. The response reflects the correct divisor as 1,760 and the correct dividend as 3,600. The solution, 2.045, is accurately rounded to 2.05 miles.
	c 6.NS.A.1	Student response is incorrect or missing. Response includes inappropriate operations, such as addition, subtraction, or multiplication.	Student response is incorrect due to inaccurate calculations when converting mixed numbers or when finding the quotients of the fractions.	Student response is correctly determined through mixed number conversion and division of fractions but is inaccurately left as a mixed number $(14\frac{5}{14})$.	Student response is accurately demonstrated through the use of visual models, such as a number line. The response is confirmed through precise mixed number conversion and division of fractions. The need for 15 bags satisfies understanding that the quotient $(14\frac{5}{14})$ is not a whole number and that 14 bags is not sufficient.
5	6.NS.B.4	Student response is incorrect or missing. Response includes inappropriate operations, such as addition, subtraction, or multiplication.	Student response is incorrect but depicts reasoning leading to finding the greatest common factor. OR Student response incorrectly utilizes division to determine the quotient of $1\frac{5}{72}$.	Student response determines that the greatest common factor of 432 and 360 is 72 through means other than the Euclidean algorithm.	Student response efficiently utilizes the Euclidean algorithm to determine the greatest common factor of 432 and 360 as 72. Response correlates the GCF to the side length of the largest square.

Name _____   Date _____

1. L.B. Johnson Middle School held a track and field event during the school year. The chess club sold various drink and snack items for the participants and the audience. Altogether, they sold 486 items that totaled $2,673.

   a. If the chess club sold each item for the same price, calculate the price of each item.

$$
\begin{array}{r}
5.5 \\
486{\overline{\smash{\big)}\,2673.0}} \\
-\underline{2430} \\
2430 \\
-\underline{2430} \\
0
\end{array}
$$

   Each item's price is $5.50.

   b. Explain the value of each digit in your answer to 1(a) using place value terms.

   $ 5 . 50

   5 ones (five dollars)

   5 tenths (five dimes)

   zero hundredths (no pennies)

Module 2:   Arithmetic Operations Including Division of Fractions

EUREKA MATH

2. The long-jump pit was recently rebuilt to make it level with the runway. Volunteers provided pieces of wood to frame the pit. Each piece of wood provided measures 6 feet, which is approximately 1.8287 meters.

2.75 meters

[rectangle diagram]

9.54 meters

a. Determine the amount of wood, in meters, needed to rebuild the frame.

$$
\begin{array}{r}
9.54\,m\\
9.54\,m\\
2.75\,m\\
+\ 2.75\,m\\
\hline
24.58\,m
\end{array}
$$

b. How many boards did the volunteers supply? Round your calculations to the nearest hundredth, and then provide the whole number of boards supplied.

$$\frac{24.58\cdot 10,000}{1.8287\cdot 10,000}=\frac{245800}{18287}$$

13.441 boards.
To have enough, the volunteers supplied 14 boards.

$$
\begin{array}{r}
13.4412\\
18287\overline{)245800.0000}\\
-18287\\
\hline
62930\\
-54861\\
\hline
80690\\
-73148\\
\hline
75420\\
-73148\\
\hline
22720\\
-18287\\
\hline
44330\\
-36574\\
\hline
7756
\end{array}
$$

3. Andy runs 436.8 meters in 62.08 seconds.

   a. If Andy runs at a constant speed, how far does he run in one second? Give your answer to the
       nearest tenth of a second.

$$\frac{436.8}{62.08}$$

Andy ran 7.0
meters in one
second.

$$\begin{array}{r} 7.03 \\ 6208\overline{)43680.00} \\ -43456 \\ \hline 2240 \\ = \quad 0 \\ \hline 22400 \\ -18624 \\ \hline 3776 \end{array}$$

   b. Use place value, multiplication with powers of 10, or equivalent fractions to explain what is
       happening mathematically to the decimal points in the divisor and dividend before dividing.

$$\frac{436.8 \cdot 100}{62.08 \cdot 100} = \frac{43680}{6,208}$$

When you write the problem
as a fraction, multiply the
numerator and denominator
by 100. Multiplying each by
100 resulted in both numbers
being whole numbers.

$436.8 \div 62.08$ is the same as $43,680 \div 6,208$.

   c. In the following expression, place a decimal point in the divisor and the dividend to create a new
       problem with the same answer as in 3(a). Then, explain how you know the answer will be the same.

$$4\ 3\ .6\ 8 \div 6\ .2\ 0\ 8$$

$$\frac{436.8}{62.08} \begin{array}{c} \div 10 \\ \div 10 \end{array} = \frac{43.68}{6.208}$$

$$\frac{43.68}{6.208} \begin{array}{c} \times 1,000 \\ \times 1,000 \end{array} = \frac{43680}{6,208}$$

Multiplying or dividing
the dividend and divisor
by the same power of
ten yields the same
quotient.

EUREKA
MATH

4. The PTA created a cross-country trail for the meet.

   a. The PTA placed a trail marker in the ground every four hundred yards. Every nine hundred yards, the PTA set up a water station. What is the shortest distance a runner will have to run to see both a water station and trail marker at the same location?

   4 (hundred)   9 (hundred)

   $\wedge$ $\wedge$

   $2 \cdot 2$ $3 \cdot 3$

   LCM $2 \cdot 2 \cdot 3 \cdot 3 = 36$ hundred

   Answer: 36 hundred yards / 3,600 yards

   b. There are 1,760 yards in one mile. About how many miles will a runner have to run before seeing both a water station and trail marker at the same location? Calculate the answer to the nearest hundredth of a mile.

$$
\begin{array}{r}
2.045 \\
1{,}760\overline{)3600.00} \\
-3520 \\
\hline
808 \\
-8000 \\
-7040 \\
\hline
9600 \\
-8800 \\
\hline
800
\end{array}
$$

   2.05 miles

   c. The PTA wants to cover the wet areas of the trail with wood chips. They find that one bag of wood chips covers a $3\frac{1}{2}$-yard section of the trail. If there is a wet section of the trail that is approximately $50\frac{1}{4}$ yards long, how many bags of wood chips are needed to cover the wet section of the trail?

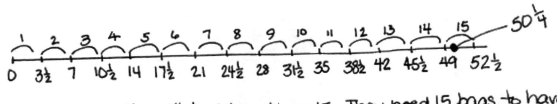

   They need more than 14 but less than 15. They need 15 bags to have enough.

   $$\frac{201}{4} \div \frac{7}{2} = \frac{201}{4} \div \frac{14}{4} = 201 \div 14 = \frac{201}{14} = 14\frac{5}{14}$$

5. The Art Club wants to paint a rectangle-shaped mural to celebrate the winners of the track and field meet. They design a checkerboard background for the mural where they will write the winners' names. The rectangle measures 432 inches in length and 360 inches in width. Use Euclid's algorithm to determine the side length of the largest square they can use to fill the checkerboard pattern completely without overlap or gaps.

length – 432 inches
width – 360 inches

$$
\begin{array}{r}
1 \\
360\overline{)432} \\
-360 \\
\hline
72
\end{array}
\qquad \text{or} \qquad
\begin{array}{r}
1 \\
360\overline{)432} \\
-360 \\
\hline
72
\end{array}
\rightarrow
\begin{array}{r}
5 \\
72\overline{)360} \\
-360 \\
\hline
0
\end{array}
$$

$432 = 360 \cdot 1 + 72$

$GCF(432, 360) = GCF(360, 72)$
$72 = 72 \checkmark$

The side length of the largest square they can use is 72 inches.

Module 2:   Arithmetic Operations Including Division of Fractions

EUREKA MATH